Build Your Own Home!

by

Michael A. Pompeii, P.E.

A concise guide to successfully subcontracting and building your own new home

ISBN 0-9711954-4-7

Printed in the United States of America

This book is dedicated to everyone who is willing to work hard and to do what it takes to get what they want.

Ordering Information:

Additional copies of this book may be ordered from Pompeii Engineers, Attn: Publications, 24 Ironwood Road, Fredericksburg VA 22405. In your request, include the number of books you wish to purchase and the intended use. Discounted rates are available and vary by quantity.

TABLE OF CONTENTS

LIST OF FIGURES

ABOUT THE AUTHOR

Michael A. Pompeii has a Bachelor's Degree in Mechanical Engineering, a Masters Degree in Systems Engineering, is a licensed Professional Engineer (P.E.), and is the founder and owner of Pompeii Engineers. He has an extensive background in the home inspection field, and is also the author of the book "Become A Home Inspector!" Many home inspectors have used this book to start up and operate their own home inspection business.

In the book "Build Your Own Home!", the author shares his knowledge, experience, and lessons-learned during his own home building experience in an easy to understand, no-nonsense way. The author combines this practical experience with his unique home inspection knowledge and experience in a step-by-step process to help readers who are interested in successfully subcontracting and building their own new home.

Chapter 1

INTRODUCTION

Subcontracting a house: *The process of hiring subcontractors, or specialists in specific trades, to build a house. The person doing the contracting, usually called the contractor or general contractor, is responsible for the overall construction planning, scheduling, coordination, hiring subcontractors, supervising the subcontractors' work, and performance of all other construction activities.*

1.1 BACKGROUND

Contracting and building your own house can be one of the most satisfying and money-saving experiences of your life. Or it can be your worst nightmare. We have all heard stories from others who have subcontracted out and built their own homes. Some say that it was a very enjoyable and rewarding experience that saved them a ton of money. But many people say that it was a constant headache and that they would never do it again. What was the difference between them? How is it that one person can totally enjoy the experience, while another totally hated it? This book focuses on what you need to do to become part of the first group.

I know what you need to do to be successful in subcontracting and building your own house because I just went through it. And you will be going through the

1

same things that I went through. There I was: I had never built or subcontracted a house before. I knew I could save a lot of money by doing the subcontracting myself. I had another full time job, and I certainly did not have the time to pound nails or install any of the major house systems myself. I was concerned and apprehensive that I was literally betting my family's home and my life savings on this being successful. What if something bad happens? How long is it going to take? How do I start? How does a construction loan work, and how do I get one? How do I find competent and reliable subcontractors? How can I organize and stay on top of a dozen things at once? I had a thousand questions, and it took a great deal of time and effort to get the right answers. That's what this book is all about- showing you the process that worked for me and sharing all the information and answers that I learned along the way.

Answers to many questions that you may have are in this book, and they will hopefully save you a lot of money, many hours of wasted time, and a good deal of unnecessary aggravation. This book takes a no-nonsense approach to contracting and building your own home and is full of real life facts, issues, situations, and lessons that I learned in the process. You will no doubt encounter many of the same things as you go through the subcontracting/building process. It is my intent, through this book, to share these lessons with you, so that you, too, can enjoy the great personal satisfaction and rewards of contracting and building your own new home. Building my house was actually fun. It was fun because I used my Home Building System that I will share with you in this book.

This book also offers another unique perspective and benefit to first time home builders. My background as a home inspector has highlighted many of the home building problems that I have seen over and over again in the many houses that I have inspected over the years. Solutions to many of these common problems are listed in this book as recommendations and "helpful hints" to prevent you from running into these same problems with your new house.

2

1.2 ADVANTAGES OF DOING IT YOURSELF

There are many advantages of subcontracting and building your own home. The most significant advantages are listed here:

1) Save money. This is by far the number one advantage of doing it yourself. In my estimation, most people are likely to save an average of 15% to 30%. Some professional builders may argue these numbers, but I know for a fact that I saved at least 27% when I built my house! These percentages add up to some very significant savings. For example, if a builder wants to charge you $250,000 to build a house on your lot, you will probably be saving somewhere between $37,500 and $75,000 if you do it yourself! This can be considered instant home equity for you, and will take a significant chunk out of your monthly mortgage payment.

2) You get to choose house plans and house styles that are just right for you. Many builders have standard sets of plans that may or may not meet your needs. If you want to customize the floor plans or style in any way, the builder will usually accommodate, but the cost of incorporating those changes will probably be more that you would be willing to pay. On the other hand, if you do some research, you can easily find a plan that has a layout and style that is exactly right for you, right from the start.

3) You get to choose building materials. This factor was very important to me when I decided to build my house because I was a home inspector who inspected many houses, and I knew what construction materials I wanted and also those materials that I did not want in my house. I wanted to specify items such as the type of foundation, the size of floor joists, the type of subflooring, the type of plumbing, the size and type of furnace and air conditioner, and a whole list of other items. After visiting many builders and getting estimates to build my house, I found that most builders will not allow you to specify the type and quality of

building materials. This is because they have standard sets of plans that are difficult to change, subcontractors who are used to using certain materials, and a certain degree of unwillingness to deviate from the current materials and methods that they use. Some builders will accommodate your requests for certain materials, but you will probably end up paying a whole lot more than your original estimate!

4) Self satisfaction. There is nothing better than being totally motivated toward a major goal, working hard toward that goal, and then achieving that goal. Most people who have successfully subcontracted and built their own home will tell you that it was one of the most satisfying and proudest accomplishments in their life. I know it was for me.

1.3 YOUR ROLE AS THE GENERAL CONTRACTOR

As stated in my definition of a general contractor at the beginning of this chapter, you will be responsible for the planning, scheduling, coordinating, hiring, and oversight of all subcontractors and their work. You, as the general contractor, will be ultimately responsible for any and all construction activities. To better understand your role, look at Figure 1-1. This chart illustrates that every phase of house construction has its own specialized subcontractors, who are experts in their own particular area, and all of these experts will be working for you. For this project, you are the boss!

How much of the actual construction work should you do yourself? As the general contractor, you should not attempt to do any major hands-on construction yourself unless you are an expert in that particular field and have plenty of free time. Just let the subcontractors do the jobs that they do everyday. They know what materials work best, the most efficient way to do things, and what is acceptable to the local building inspectors.

4

Believe me, you will have plenty of work to do everyday without even pounding a nail. You will be busy lining up and coordinating subcontractor after subcontractor, constantly checking their work, cleaning up, more cleaning up, getting supplies, doing small odd jobs, calling suppliers, and constantly adapting to changes. You will be busy!

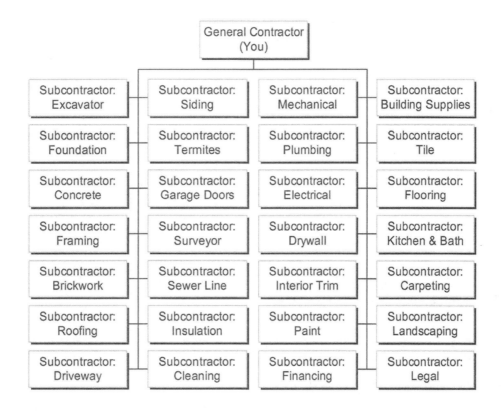

Figure 1-1. The General Contractor's relationship to Subcontractors.

1.4 A SYSTEMS APPROACH TO HOME BUILDING

This book describes and uses a home building and subcontracting system that I developed and successfully used to build my new home. The system is based on a logical, simple to use, and simple to understand approach that uses requirements, schedules, checklists, and phased construction. You will learn the specifics of this system simply by following and using the information provided in this book. The numerous, complex, and somewhat overwhelming efforts required to build your house are broken down into small, manageable pieces that will allow you to proceed from one step to the next with relative ease. The basic system that will be used is as follows:

1) Get yourself into the right mindset.

2) Determine and WRITE DOWN the requirements for your house.

3) Find the appropriate building lot.

4) Select the right house plan the meets your requirements.

5) Develop detailed schedules as shown in this book.

6) Get a construction loan.

7) Get permits.

8) Line up and schedule subcontractors.

9) Start Phase 1 of construction as shown in this book.

10) Continue through all 6 Phases of construction until completion.

By using the system presented in this book, every part of the home building process becomes tied together and integrated as a "system", and helps you to schedule the right thing at the right time. This goal of this systems approach is to end up with a completed house where every individual system was designed and built to seamlessly work with every other individual system in the house. This results in a house that is finished on schedule, within your budget, meets your specific needs, and in the end, a home that you will be completely happy with and that will make you proud.

I developed and used this system to build the house shown in Figure 1-2, and my family and I are extremely happy with our new home and the entire home building experience. I am not showing you a photo of this home to try to impress you or to show off, but rather to show you that someone just like you or me, who has never subcontracted and built a house before, can not only build their own home and save thousands of dollars, but also have fun in the process. The methods and processes in this book will show you how.

Figure 1-2. The house that I subcontracted and built using the system presented in this book.

This book includes many checklists, budget forms, planning forms, and schedule forms that are absolutely critical to coordinating the construction. Each phase of planning and construction has its own schedule, checklist, or other specific information for you to follow and use, and helps to guide you on WHAT you need to do and WHEN you need to do it. By using this approach, expert technical knowledge in homebuilding is not required. The only technical knowledge that is needed to use this system is a general and basic level of understanding of the house systems (i.e., foundation, framing, mechanical, plumbing, electrical, etc.).

It is important to note that the home building system presented in this book is based on building a home in central Virginia. Building practices will vary in different parts of the country, but the basics will remain the same. For example, my house was built with a full basement, with walls made of poured concrete. But other areas of the country use foundations with concrete slabs, pilings, or crawlspaces. Regardless of the building practices used in your area, the home building system used in this book has built in flexibility to allow you to adapt to the type of construction that you will need to use. In addition, the local contractors in your area may have their own customary ways of doing things that may be slightly different than the procedures outlined in this book. That's okay because you need to allow the contractors to use their experience and to work in the way that they have found that works best for them.

1.5 USING THIS SYSTEM

The best way to use this book is to first read it thoroughly, then copy the blank schedule sheets and fill them in with your own first rough schedule. Use my filled in schedules as a guide. These schedules will help you to identify any areas that you are not comfortable with or where you may need more information. For example, if you are not comfortable with your knowledge of electrical wiring, then go and get and study some additional books or information that covers residential electrical systems. Remember, you do not need to know everything about electrical systems, but rather just enough to understand the basics of how the electrical system works and how it goes together. Leave the details to your hired experts--- your subcontractors.

As you go through the process outlined in this book, you will gain more and more knowledge and information. Then you will revise your schedule again and again. This is a good thing because an accurate schedule is a major and critical part

8

of this home building system and this will be the main tool to guide you successfully through the homebuilding process.

But before you do any additional research or scheduling, you need to find out if you have what takes to be successful in subcontracting and building your own new home. If you want to be successful, it is not enough to just have construction knowledge or experience. You must also have the right mindset to deal with the tough and relentless job of planning, scheduling, meetings, phone calls, dealing with changes and problems, and coordinating all work activities. On top of that, you will probably be juggling your other full-time job and family concerns at the same time. But you can do it, and this area is covered in the next chapter.

Chapter 2

DO YOU HAVE WHAT IT TAKES?

The very first thing that you need to do is to sit down and realize what it is going to take to be successful in building your new home. Remember, you want this to be an enjoyable and rewarding experience, and not a situation that will cause headaches, despair, and divorce. How do you do it? After many trials and tribulations, I found that the answer boils down to six critical factors: attitude, planning and organization, communication skills, competence, decisiveness, and action. These six factors are explained below.

2.1 ATTITUDE

You must approach building and contracting your own house with an optimistic, realistic, and fun attitude. If you go into this with an attitude of "I'm going to hate this!" or "I can't wait until this is over", then just stop right now because you are doomed to a miserable experience. Go hire a builder, and let him or her do the work. On the other hand, if you go into it with an "I'm going to have fun doing this" or "this will be a great experience" attitude, then you have just drastically increased your probability of success. I'm not kidding here, and I can't overemphasize how important your overall attitude is before and during the process. Some readers are probably now saying to themselves "OK, if I wanted a psychology lesson, I would have got a psychology book." But they are missing the point--- the goal of this book is to make you successful at contracting and building your own house, and to do that, an optimistic and enthusiastic attitude is absolutely essential. You will certainly run into some anxiety caused by problems and setbacks, but resolve now to not let those problems or setbacks control you. Right from the start, expect to work hard, realize that problems will come up, and commit to yourself that you will calmly and competently solve them, no matter what they are. You can do it--- it's not as hard as you may think!

2.2 PLANNING AND ORGANIZING

You must have the ability, willingness, and the right tools to constantly plan and organize. When I say tools here, I am not talking about hammers and screwdrivers, but proper work schedules, planning charts, documentation, and filing systems. Proper planning is absolutely essential for success, and will make things run unbelievably smooth. Proper planning means that every drawing, every room, every stairway, every wall, every door, and every other item in the house has been carefully thought out and accurately represented in any drawing or other documentation and paperwork that you may have.

You will acquire a great deal of paper in the planning and building process, and it is critical to keep it organized so that you know exactly where every piece of paper is, so that you can immediately pull that paper out when you need it. Examples of the paperwork that you will accumulate include house drawings, numerous revisions of house drawings, individual changes to individual drawings, survey plats, truss drawings, product literature, permit paperwork, cost estimates, bank statements, financial information, lien waivers, lumberyard accounts, house schedules, revised house schedules, work proposals, bills, receipts--- the paperwork will seem endless. If you vow from the start to develop a file system and to constantly keep it organized as things come in, you will save yourself many headaches and many hours of searching for papers that you need at critical times.

2.3 COMMUNICATION SKILLS

You must be able to constantly and effectively communicate your wants and needs to a wide range of people that have a wide range of knowledge and skill. You must be as effective at talking to the president of the bank as you are with talking to a young minimum wage laborer working at your building site. Poor communication is perhaps the most common cause of mistakes in homebuilding and remodeling, so you must always have very frequent and frank discussions with each and every person you deal with in the process. This is especially important for the subcontractors at the building site. Don't let anyone start anything until you meet the boss or foreman on site, and carefully go over every detail of what you want. Always be just a phone call away if the subcontractor runs into any problems or has any questions, and always check all of the work at the house on a daily basis. The sooner you catch a mistake, the better it is for all involved. Also, don't assume that the contractor can read your mind, and don't be afraid to speak up if you see something that may be wrong! You always want to be nice, but certainly not to the point where you let mistakes be made. Good communication skills also mean that you treat everyone with common courtesy and respect, no matter who they are or what their job is. This will pay big dividends for you, your subcontractors, and your new house.

2.4 COMPETENCE

You do not need to be an expert in all aspects of house building, but you do need to have a certain level of competence in the house construction process. You need to learn enough so that you can speak the same language and be on the same terms with your subcontractors. For example, when your framing subcontractor talks about joists, beams, and headers, you need to know what the difference is between each one. When your plumber talks about supply, waste, and vent lines, you need to understand what he is talking about. There is no need to become an expert in every single area, but there is a need to be a generalist, where you know a little about each system in the house, whether it be the foundation, framing, mechanical, plumbing, electrical, etc. If you are not confident in your current home construction knowledge, you can gain this competence by reading and studying the many books and web sites that are readily available on house construction.

2.5 DECISIVENESS

You must be able to make on the spot decisions quickly and accurately. If you are the kind of person that frets over the smallest things and cannot make decisions quickly, then you may want to consider just hiring a builder. As the contractor, you will be meeting with subcontractors who will be asking you detailed questions, and your answers must be given quickly because the subcontractors do not have the time to wait around for you to make a decision. This on the spot decision making may not be as tough as you may think. This is because by the time the subcontractors arrive, you will know every detail in the house plans because you have already gone through the plans and options over and over again. This will make most of your decisions easy.

2.6 ACTION

You must make a commitment to yourself that you will always take action to get things done quickly. Realize that you will be extremely busy, and it will be tough to resist the temptation to take a few days off here and there. If your regular job has you working days on Monday through Friday, you can bet that you will be at the house every weekend for 12 hours a day, and almost every single week day night. There will most likely be times that you are tired and don't feel like making those phone calls or following your schedule. The time that your house is going up is no time to be lazy. You must always be ready to make that next phone call or to meet with another subcontractor. You have a much greater chance of success in subcontracting and homebuilding if you resolve to take action on any situation, to take that action quickly, and to be relentless.

2.7 CAN YOU DO IT?

Carefully study and seriously think about these six factors. If you believe that you will not be able to fully meet any one or more of these factors, then you must seriously consider just turning this job over to an experienced home builder, and let them do the work. You won't save as much money or be as involved in the decision making process, but by studying this book, you will at least be much more knowledgeable in the home building process and in your dealings with the builder. On the other hand, if you believe that the above six factors will not be a problem, then congratulations! You are ready to move on and to get the home building process going. This process starts in the next chapter.

Chapter 3

CHOOSING YOUR BUILDING LOT

Deciding on your land or building lot is not as easy as you might think. There are many things to consider, such as zoning requirements, accessibility and right of way, lot size, easements and setbacks, slope and drainage, soil stability, soil percolation (for septic systems), well water, and availability of utilities. Don't even think about buying your lot until you have thoroughly checked into and answered each of the following questions:

a. Zoning Requirements.

- Is the lot zoned for residential construction?

- Is there a minimum or maximum house size that you can build?

- Are there any homeowner association covenants in effect?

- Are separate garages or outbuildings allowed?

b. Accessibility and Right of Way.

- Is there access to the lot from a main road?

- If there is no direct road access, is there a right of way provision to allow you to build your access road over an adjoining property?

- Are there any department of transportation requirements for building an access road or driveway?

c. Lot Size, Easements, and Setbacks.

- Is the lot large enough for the type of house you desire?

- Are there any utility easements on the lot that may limit where you can build your house?

- Are there any rules for how far your house must set back from the street or from adjacent properties?

d. Slope and Drainage.

- Will the lot support a sufficient slope so that water will effectively drain away from the foundation?

- Is the lot in a flood plain?

- Will the lot allow a house location that is not in a low lying area that will encounter basement or foundation water problems?

e. Soil Stability.

- Is the underlying soil stable enough to support your home?

- Does the area have any previous history of soil stability problems (i.e., sink holes, shrink-swell clay soil, underground water, etc.)?

f. Soil Percolation.

- If an underground septic system will be used, does the soil allow enough water percolation to use a septic drainfield (i.e., does the soil "perc") for the house size that you require?

g. Well Water.

- If a municipal water supply is not available, is there sufficient underground water available for a well, and will the well be of reasonable depth?

- Is there a history or a possibility of groundwater contamination in the area?

h. Availability of Utilities.

- Is electricity, phone service, municipal water and sewer, natural gas, and/or cable television available in the area?

- If not, will it be prohibitively expense to bring those services to your lot?

i. Legal Issues.

- Is there a clear title for the land?

- Are there any liens on or disputes over the land?

- Are neighbors okay?

- Are there any future roadways, airports, landfills, etc. that are coming on or near the lot?

- Do you have a competent real estate lawyer to help you to avoid any other issues that may be present, and to help with the paperwork in purchasing the lot?

j. Other issues that may affect the specific lot or property?

All of the above issues are shown in a checklist format at Figure 3-1. Copy and use this checklist for each lot or property that you are considering.

Once all of these questions are answered and you are satisfied that the lot will meet your requirements for building a house, then you may proceed with buying the lot and starting the house planning process. The planning process starts with the house plans, which is covered in the next chapter.

BUILDING LOT CHECKLIST

- ❏ Zoned for residential use
- ❏ Utility easements
- ❏ House set back requirements
- ❏ Access to lot
- ❏ D.O.T. requirements
- ❏ Flood plain or drainage issues
- ❏ Slope
- ❏ Percolation for septic system
- ❏ Well water available
- ❏ Stable soil
- ❏ Municipal water and sewer availability
- ❏ Electricity availability
- ❏ Telephone availability
- ❏ Cable TV availability
- ❏ Natural gas availability
- ❏ Clear title
- ❏ Liens or disputes
- ❏ Neighbors
- ❏ Future roadways, airports, landfills
- ❏ Other _____
- ❏ Other _____

Figure 3-1. Building Lot Checklist.

Chapter 4

HOUSE PLANS

4.1 DETERMINE YOUR REQUIREMENTS

Before you start to look at house plans, you must first take some time to identify and to write down your requirements for your new house. What is it that you really want and need with the new house? You must talk to your family to see what they want and need, and this includes everything from something as general as the style of the house to something as detailed as how big the closets will be. Believe me, taking a lot of time to thoroughly think about and go through this house requirements list will probably be the most valuable time you will spent in the whole house building process. Why? Because you will end up with a house that suits your needs and a house that will make you and your family very happy.

Here is a checklist to help you to think about and to determine your own unique wants and needs for your new house:

- ❑ How much house can I afford?
- ❑ Do you want one, two, or three levels?
- ❑ What style do you want? (Examples include Ranch, Colonial, Tudor, Contemporary, Rustic, Farmhouse, Executive, etc.)

21

- Do you want a front porch? If so, do you want it to be open or covered?
- Do you want a garage? If so, how many cars need to fit?
- Do you want a workshop in the garage?
- Do you need a storage area in the garage?
- Do you need or want an oversized garage?
- Where will you store your lawn mower, yard equipment, etc.?
- Do you want the garage attached or detached from the house?
- Do you want a vestibule, half bath, or closet coming in from the garage?
- Where do you want the laundry room to be located?
- How many bedrooms do you need?
- What size is acceptable for each bedroom?
- Is the master bedroom on the first or second floor?
- Do you need a guest or spare bedroom?
- How much closet space do you need in each bedroom?
- How many bathrooms do you need, and where do those bathrooms need to be located?
- How large does the kitchen need to be?
- Do you want an eat-in kitchen or do you want a separate dining room?
- Do you want a family room or a more formal living room, or both?
- If so, how large do the family room or living room need to be?
- Do you want a den or study?
- Do you need a separate home office?
- If you have a basement, do you want any finished living areas?
- Do you need a small or a large storage area?
- Do you need room for exercise equipment?
- Do you need room for a pool table or similar?
- Do you want a deck or patio? If so, do you want it to be open or covered?
- How large of a lawn area do you need?
- Other needs not covered above?

Once you think about and thoroughly discuss this checklist with your spouse or family, you MUST write down exactly what you need. Call this piece of paper your "New House Requirements List." You will use this list to help you find and/or design the right set of house plans. The requirements list that I used for my new house is shown as an example at Figure 4-1. Use this as an example or template for your own requirements list. Again, this list is extremely important because it forms the entire basis for the home building process, so DO NOT SKIP THIS STEP!

4.2 INITIAL COST ESTIMATE

You will now need to determine: 1) how much house you can afford (or are willing to pay), and 2) an initial cost estimate for building your new house. Armed with this information, you will be able to determine what requirements you may need to trade off in order for you to afford the house you desire. Obviously, you cannot build what you cannot afford.

A rough estimate of what you can afford is all that is needed at this point. Most people can do this with simple mortgage calculators that consider how much money you make, how long the mortgage will be (usually 15 or 30 years), and what the interest rate will be. Perhaps the easiest way to do this is to go to an internet search engine and search for "mortgage calculator". You will find many free services in the results. If you do not have access to the internet, just visit your local bank and they can usually provide a simple mortgage table for you.

If you have credit issues or are just unsure of what you can afford, then it is a good idea to get pre-approved for a loan before you go any further in the home building process. Construction loans and mortgages are discussed in more detail in Chapter 5.

Figure 4-1. My New House Requirements List

General
- Colonial style
- attached garage
- large covered deck at rear
- concrete patio at rear

Master Bedroom and Bathroom
- BIG walk-in closet
- separate his & her sinks
- whirlpool tub
- large room
- located near kid's bedrooms

Kid's Bedrooms
- 3 large bedrooms
- one with own bathroom
- two with shared bathroom for boys

My Office
- in finished basement
- has egress windows
- can be considered an extra bedroom

Basement
- Mostly finished living area
- 10 x 12 exercise room
- bar area with sink
- extra family room/play area
- large unfinished room for storage
- walk out basement
- as many windows as possible
- one full bathroom

Garage
- 3 car garage
- 2 bays for cars, 1 for bikes, etc.
- side load
- space for a workbench
- walk out door
- automatic door openers
- driveway has space to park 2 cars

Kitchen
- large eating area
- breakfast bar with 4 stools
- nice appliances
- quiet dishwasher
- large pantry closet
- sink has large window to back yard

Interior
- hardwood floors in living room and
  dining room
- hardwood steps to upper level
- lots of crown molding

Utility Room
- located near entrance from garage
- space for washer/dryer
- large coat/shoe closet
- half bath located nearby

Guest Bedroom
- located away from main bedrooms on first
floor or in finished basement
- Full bathroom close by

Other
- quiet bath fans
- quiet range hood
- high efficiency gas furnace
- large hot water heater
- gas logs in family room
- 40 or 50 year shingles for roof
- sound insulation for plumbing pipes
- separate air returns in each bedroom
- no bounce in any floors
- all gutters/downspouts have extensions to
take water at least 15 feet from foundation
- landscaping designed to minimize
maintenance
- little or no painting for exterior

How do you do an initial cost estimate for your new house? There are several ways of doing this, but perhaps the easiest and most accurate way is by doing cost comparisons of new homes going up in your area. The cost comparison process goes like this:

1. Obtain pricing information for houses similar to yours from local builders. Perhaps the best way to do this is to visit model homes and collect their literature and price information.

2. Find out the approximate price for the lot itself (with no house).

3. Subtract the cost of the lot from the builders selling price of the house. For example:

> - Builder's price for house and lot is $238,000
> - Cost of lot itself is about $45,000
> - Builder's cost to build house is $238,000 - $45,000 = $193,000

4. Divide builder's cost for the house itself by the square feet of living area in the house. This will give you the cost per square foot that the local builder is charging. For example:

> - Builder's cost of house is $193,000
> - Square footage is 2250 square feet
> - $193,000 / 2250 = approximately $85/sqft

5. Assuming a builder's markup, handling fees, salary and profit of 20%, multiply the cost per square foot in step 4 by 80% (multiply by 0.80). Depending on the area that you live in, this figure can range from 5% to 30%. For example:

- Builder's cost is approximately $85/sqft

- Builder's fee approximately 20%.

- $85/sqft times 0.80 = approximately $68/sqft

6. Multiply the cost per square foot estimate from step 5 with the square footage from the house size that you are considering. For example:

- Local building cost is approximately $68/sqft

- Your house plan is 2480 square feet

- $68/sqft multiplied by 2480 sqft = approximately $169,000

7. Add the cost of your lot to the approximate cost of the house from step 7. For example:

- Cost of your lot is $71,000

- Approximate cost to build house is $169,000

- Total cost will be approximately $71,000 + $169,000 = $240,000

If you follow this cost comparison process, the number you come up with will be a good initial estimate of what your new house is going to cost AND how much money you are probably going to save by being your own builder.

4.3 FIND THE RIGHT HOUSE PLAN

House plans are available through books at the library, in bookstores, in building supply stores, and on the internet. Custom house plans are also available from local architects or draftsmen that specialize in house design. The internet is a terrific place to start your search. Just go to a search engine, type in "house plans", and browse through the many web pages that list and sell house plans. You can literally browse through thousands of styles and floor plans in your price range to find the plans that you like, and to get some good ideas on other features you may not have considered.

When you find a design with a floor plan that you really like, go through each item on your requirements list to determine if that particular design fits your written requirements. This is important, so don't skip this step! Don't get trapped by falling in love with the exterior design of the house, only to move in and live with a miserable floor plan that does not fit your needs.

If you find a design that meets all the items on your house requirements list, then just go ahead and purchase those house plans. If the design does not meet all of the requirements, which will probably be the case, then you need to determine if minor modifications to the design or floor plan can be made. If the changes you need are very minor, then you may be able to make the changes yourself. But be aware that any changes you make may have a significant impact on other drawings, and could cause you major problems during construction. So if you are uncomfortable with making changes, or if the changes are significant, then making changes is best left up to an architect or draftsman who specializes in residential construction. If you are still unsure or just do not know enough about what house drawings will meet your requirements, then you are strongly advised to seek the assistance of a licensed architect who specializes in residential construction.

Here is what I did for my house. I searched through many house designs on the internet, and found a design that my family and I really liked that was within our general price range. But the floor plan needed some significant changes to meet our requirements list. For example, we needed the whole floor plan to be reversed (or mirrored), more closet space in the master bedroom, separate sinks in the master bathroom, a three car garage instead of a two car garage, a partially finished basement with an office area and a spare bedroom, rearrangement of the

27

kitchen area, and some other minor interior and exterior changes. Because these changes were significant, I sketched out my own floor plans and took them to a local draftsman who did this type of work for a living. That was a very good decision, because the draftsman found and corrected many items that I would have never thought of until it was too late. We went through at least five complete rounds of reviewing draft drawings, coming up with new changes, then doing it all again. This review process is extremely valuable because it forces you to thoroughly think through every single detail and dimension in the house. It also helps to catch any mistakes, because a critical mistake on the drawing that shows up during construction can end up costing you a whole lot of extra money. The bottom line: If you want to save yourself time and money and avoid aggravation, thoroughly check and re-check every single detail and dimension in every single drawing. Trust me- you will be glad you did.

4.4 OTHER REQUIRED DRAWINGS

A typical standard set of house drawings may not be enough. You will also need detailed engineering drawings of the floor system (joist size, joist spans, joist spacing, joist location, stair supports, load bearing wall supports), headers (the support structure above windows and doors), and roof trusses. An example of the overall roof truss drawings that were used for my house are shown in Figure 4-2. All drawings that show engineered roof trusses, engineered joists or flooring systems, and engineered headers or support beams must be approved and sealed (or stamped) by a licensed Professional Engineer (P.E.) or architect.

If you did not receive these drawings with your house plans, do not worry. You can usually get these engineered drawings for free, just like I did. Just find a good local lumberyard or building supply store that have special accounts and salespersons that cater strictly to home builders. These suppliers usually have an

28

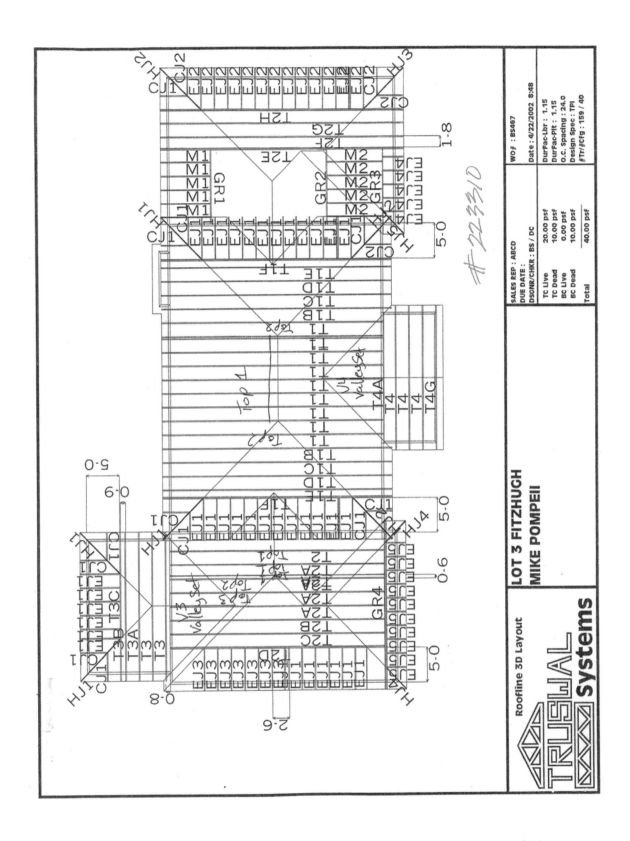

Figure 4-2. An example of an engineered roof truss drawing (page 1 of 3).

BATCHJOB:BS467
Date: 4/22/2002
Company Name
Address
city, TX 76011
1-800-521-9790
Sales Rep:ABCD
Designer:BS

Quote# BS467
MIKE POMPEII

Job:LOT 3 FITZHUGH

Loading:20 10 10 24.00"O.C.

ITEM	QTY	TRUSS ID		SPAN	PITCH	OVERHANGS		PRICE
1	12	CJ1 24.00"OC 0' 4" 9		4' 0" 7 3' 8"15	10.00/0.00 12 CORNERJACKS	0.00/ 0.00 CL1 CR0		
2	4	CJ2 24.00"OC 0' 4" 9		4' 0" 7 3' 8"15	10.00/0.00 4 CORNERJACKS	0.00/ 0.00 CL10400 CR0		
3	39	EJ1 24.00"OC 0' 4" 9		6' 0" 0 5' 4" 9	10.00/0.00 39 ENDJACKS	0.00/ 0.00 CL1 CR0		
4	14	EJ2 24.00"OC 0' 4" 9		6' 0" 0 5' 4" 9	10.00/0.00 14 ENDJACKS	0.00/ 0.00 CL10400 CR0		
5	7	EJ3 24.00"OC 0' 4" 9		6' 0" 0 3'10" 9	10.00/0.00 7 TRAYED ENDJACKS	0.00/ 0.00 CL1 CR0		
6	5	EJ4 24.00"OC 0' 4" 9		3' 2" 8 3' 0"10	10.00/0.00 5 ENDJACKS	0.00/ 0.00 CL10400 CR0		
7	10	EJ5 24.00"OC 0' 4" 9		2'11" 8 2'10" 2	10.00/0.00 10 ENDJACKS	0.00/ 0.00 CL10400 CR0		
8	1	GR1 24.00"OC 6' 5" 0		10' 9" 8 6' 5" 0	0.00/0.00 1 1-PLY BOX GIRDER	0.00/ 0.00		
9	1	GR2 24.00"OC 7' 2" 0		10' 9" 8 7' 2" 0	0.00/0.00 1 1-PLY BOX GIRDER	0.00/ 0.00		
10	1	GR3 24.00"OC 0' 4" 9		2' 5" 0 3' 0"10	10.00/0.00 1 1-PLY GIRDER	0.00/ 0.00 CL10400 CR0		
11	3	GR4 24.00"OC 0' 4" 9		24' 4" 0 0' 4" 9	10.00/0.00 1 3-PLY GIRDER	0.00/ 0.00 CL1 CR10400		
12	4	HJ1 24.00"OC 0' 4" 9		8' 5"13 5' 4" 9	7.07/0.00 4 HIPJACKS	0.00/ 0.00 CL10500 CR0		
13	3	HJ2 24.00"OC 0' 4" 9		8' 5"13 5' 4" 9	7.07/0.00 3 HIPJACKS	0.00/ 0.00 CL10902 CR0		
14	1	HJ3 24.00"OC 0' 4" 9		8' 5"13 5' 4" 9	7.07/0.00 1 HIPJACK	0.00/ 0.00 CL11010 CR0		
15	2	HJ4 24.00"OC 0' 4" 9		4' 2" 3 2'10" 2	7.07/0.00 2 HIPJACKS	0.00/ 0.00 CL11010 CR0		
16	1	HJ5 24.00"OC 0' 4" 9		4' 6" 7 3' 0"10	7.07/0.00 1 HIPJACK	0.00/ 0.00 CL20202 CR0		

Figure 4-2. An example of an engineered roof truss drawing (page 2 of 3).

30

ITEM	QTY	TRUSS ID	SPAN	PITCH	OVERHANGS	PRICE
17	5	M1 24.00"OC 0' 4" 9	7' 4" 8 6' 6" 5	10.00/0.00 5 MONOS	0.00/ 0.00 CL1 CR0	
18	5	M2 24.00"OC 0' 4" 9	8' 4" 0 7' 3"14	10.00/0.00 5 MONOS	0.00/ 0.00	
19	8	T1 TOP1 24.00"OC 0' 4" 9	6' 9" 7 0' 4" 9	10.00/0.00 8 PIGGYBACK TOPS	7.27/ 7.27	
20	2	T1 TOP2 24.00"OC 0' 4" 9	6' 9" 7 0' 4" 9	10.00/0.00 2 PIGGYBACK TOPS	7.27/ 7.27	
21	10	T1 24.00"OC 1' 5"14	33' 0" 0 0' 4" 9	10.00/0.00 STUBBED REGULAR	0.00/ 0.00 CL0 CR1	
22	2	T1B 24.00"OC 0' 4" 9	34' 4" 0 0' 4" 9	10.00/0.00 2 STEPDOWNS	0.00/ 0.00 CL10400 CR1	
23	2	T1C 24.00"OC 0' 4" 9	34' 4" 0 0' 4" 9	10.00/0.00 2 STEPDOWNS	0.00/ 0.00 CL10400 CR1	
24	2	T1D 24.00"OC 0' 4" 9	34' 4" 0 0' 4" 9	10.00/0.00 2 STEPDOWNS	0.00/ 0.00 CL10400 CR1	
25	2	T1E 24.00"OC 0' 4" 9	34' 4" 0 0' 4" 9	10.00/0.00 2 STEPDOWNS	0.00/ 0.00 CL10400 CR1	
26	4	T1F 24.00"OC 0' 4" 9	34' 4" 0 0' 4" 9	10.00/0.00 2 2-PLY HIPGIRDERS	0.00/ 0.00 CL10400 CR1	
27	3	T2 TOP1 24.00"OC 0' 4" 9	7' 9" 7 0' 4" 9	10.00/0.00 3 PIGGYBACK TOPS	7.27/ 7.27	
28	1	T2 TOP2 24.00"OC 0' 4" 9	7' 9" 7 0' 4" 9	10.00/0.00 1 PIGGYBACK TOP	7.27/ 7.27	
29	1	T2 TOP3 24.00"OC 0' 4" 9	7' 9" 7 0' 4" 9	10.00/0.00 1 PIGGYBACK TOP	7.27/ 7.27	
30	6	T2 42.00"OC 0' 4" 9	32' 0" 0 1' 2" 9	10.00/0.00 1 STUBBED REGULAR	0.00/ 0.00	
31	5	T2A 24.00"OC 0' 4" 9	32' 0" 0 1' 2" 9	10.00/0.00 5 STUBBED TRAYS	0.00/ 0.00	
32	1	T2B 24.00"OC 0' 4" 9	32' 0" 0 1' 2" 9	10.00/0.00 1 STUBBED TRAY	0.00/ 0.00	
33	1	T2C 24.00"OC 0' 4" 9	32' 0" 0 1' 2" 9	10.00/0.00 1 STUBBED TRAY	0.00/ 0.00	
34	2	T2D 24.00"OC 3' 1"14	32' 0" 0 1' 2" 9	10.00/0.00 1 2-PLY GIRDER	0.00/ 0.00	
35	2	T2E 24.00"OC 0' 4" 9	36' 4" 0 0' 4" 9	10.00/0.00 1 2-PLY GIRDER	0.00/ 0.00 CL10400 CR1	
36	1	T2F 24.00"OC 0' 4" 9	36' 4" 0 0' 4" 9	10.00/0.00 1 STEPDOWN	0.00/ 0.00 CL10400 CR1	
37	1	T2G 24.00"OC 0' 4" 9	36' 4" 0 0' 4" 9	10.00/0.00 1 STEPDOWN	0.00/ 0.00 CL10400 CR1	
38	2	T2H 24.00"OC 0' 4" 9	36' 4" 0 0' 4" 9	10.00/0.00 1 2-PLY HIPGIRDER	0.00/ 0.00 CL10400 CR1	
39	2	T3 24.00"OC 0' 4" 9	21' 6" 0 0' 4" 9	10.00/0.00 2 REGULAR	0.00/ 0.00 CL1 CR1	

Figure 4-2. An example of an engineered roof truss drawing (page 3 of 3).

experienced draftsman on their staff who uses special software that specifically designs your own custom floor, header, and truss systems. As long as you purchase your materials from that supplier, these design services and drawings will most likely be free of charge. Plus, it gives you several less things to worry about.

The relationship you have with your salesperson at your supply yard can be one of the most time saving and cost effective items that you will have. This important supplier arrangement is discussed further in Chapter 8.

The final drawing that is required is your house plat. The plat is usually a single drawing, developed by a licensed surveyor, that shows the exact location of your house (and your drain field, if necessary) on the lot. An example of a plat is shown in Figure 4-3. This plat is critical because it will help to ensure that you are building within the utility easements and setbacks required for that lot. The last thing you need is to find out that you built your house in an illegal location on your lot!

With all drawings in hand, the next step is to investigate and secure a construction loan. This is covered in the next chapter.

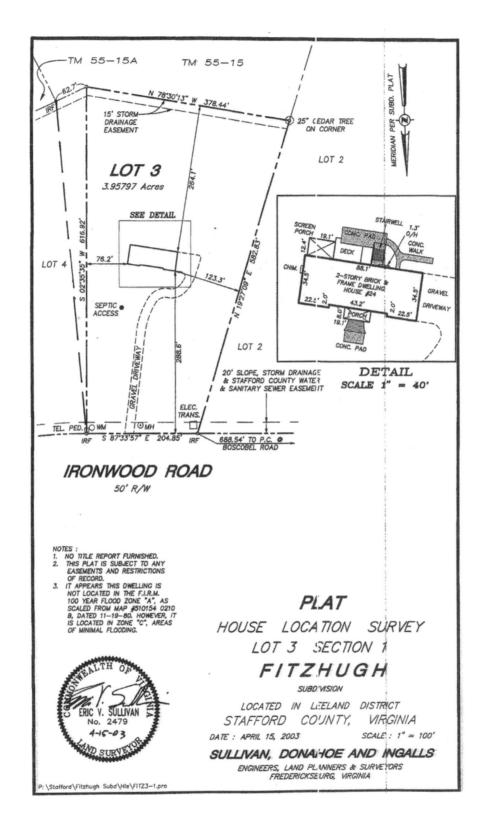

Figure 4-3. An example of a plat drawing.

Chapter 5

CONSTRUCTION LOANS, MORTGAGES, AND INSURANCE

5.1 TYPES OF CONSTRUCTION LOANS

There are many types and varieties of construction loans. Any mortgage company or bank that deals in construction loans can help you to determine what specific type of construction loan is best for you in your situation. The type of loan that worked best for me was called a "construction-permanent" or "construction-perm" loan.

In a construction-perm loan, the amount you borrow to construct your house automatically rolls over to a permanent mortgage once your house is completed. There are some major advantages to this type of loan, including paying settlement fees only one time and minimizing all the paperwork by doing it only one time. If you do not have this type of construction loan, but rather a typical construction loan, you would have to apply for the construction loan, go to settlement and pay the settlement fees for the construction loan, then apply for a mortgage loan, then go to settlement and pay the settlement fees for the mortgage loan. That is a lot of fees, a lot of paperwork, and a lot of trips to the bank or mortgage company. When

35

you are building your own house, you will not have much time for any extra trips or work. It is in your best interest to keep things as simple as possible, which is why a construction-perm loan may be your best bet. The less things you have to worry about during the construction process, the better. *This is exactly why you need to let the experts in a certain area do their job and work for you. It will not only make your life easier, it will save you money.*

5.2 HOW THE DRAW SYSTEM WORKS

Here is how the construction loan and mortgage process worked for me. Your experience will probably be very similar, so use this as a guide:

1. Ask friends or associates for a referral for good, dependable, responsive, local banks or mortgage companies.

2. Call and schedule an appointment with the bank or mortgage company to discuss your construction loan options.

3. Decide if you are comfortable with the mortgage company.

4. If comfortable, submit a loan application and preliminary paperwork.

5. The mortgage company will provide you with a maximum loan amount for which you qualify. If you are comfortable that you can build your new home for less than this amount, then you can proceed. However, if the cost estimate for building your new home is more than the amount you qualified for, then you must either go back and trade off some of your written requirements, or, in the worst case, find a new and cheaper house plan.

6. Once the loan application is approved, submit your house drawings, lot plans, and a list of your construction cost estimates with as many subcontractors (by name) as possible on the special construction loan/budget forms supplied by the mortgage company. A typical construction loan/budget form is shown at Figure 5-1 for you to copy and use, and a completed 3-page form (for the first draw) is shown at Figure 5-2 as an example for you to follow.

7. Once your cost estimates and building plans are approved, schedule a "loan closing" or "loan settlement" with a good, local real estate attorney. This attorney should also serve as your "lien agent", which is further discussed in item 10, below.

8. Your mortgage company will work with your attorney to develop your "closing package".

9. You attend the closing, sign all of the paperwork, and pay the closing fees.

10. You are now eligible to make withdrawals or "draws" from your construction loan to pay your subcontractors. Every time you make a draw, you will need to submit the construction loan/budget form that you developed (or a similar one that may be supplied by the mortgage company), along with all receipts that you need payment for. After the first draw, you will also have to submit "lien waivers" for the major cost items in your draw request. A lien waiver is basically a piece of paper that is signed by the subcontractor stating that he/she was paid for the work they did. These lien waivers will be collected and processed by your attorney (i.e., your lien agent) for your legal and financial protection. The mortgage company will want you to have all major subcontractors sign the lien waiver at the time that you pay the subcontractor. A sample lien waiver is shown at

37

CONSTRUCTION LOAN TRACKING SCHEDULE

Date: _____
DRAW NUMBER: _____

Builder's Name: _____
House Location: _____

Item #	Activity	Estimated Cost	Actual Cost for this Draw	Actual Cost to Date	Cost to Complete	Percent Complete	Contractor Name & Phone
TOTALS							

PAGE ____

Figure 5-1. Budget and Construction Loan Form for you to copy and use.

CONSTRUCTION LOAN TRACKING SCHEDULE

Date: 25 JULY
DRAW NUMBER: 1

Builder's Name: MICHAEL POMPEII
House Location: 24 IRONWOOD ROAD

Item #	Activity	Estimated Cost	Actual Cost for this Draw	Actual Cost to Date	Cost to Complete	Percent Complete	Contractor Name & Phone
A	PRELIMINARY COST						
1	PLANS	850	850	850	0	100%	S.C. DRAFTING
2	PERMITS	3208	3310	3310	0	100%	STAFFORD COUNTY
3	SURVEY	200	150	150	0	100%	SDI, INC.
4	APPRAISAL	250	250	250	0	100%	SUNTRUST MORTGAGE
5	WATER HOOKUP	4140					STAFFORD COUNTY
6	SEWER HOOKUP	4040					STAFFORD COUNTY
7	INSURANCE	700	750	750	0	100%	STATE FARM
8	LEGAL FEES	300					ATTORNEY
	TOTAL	13,688					
B	LOT PREPARATION						
1	CLEARING	500	400	400	0	100%	TOP LINE EXCAVATING
2	EXCAVATION	1650	1100	1100	550	67%	''
3	EROSION CONTROL	600	600	600	0	100%	''
4	DRIVEWAY PREP	520	520	520	0	100%	''
	TOTAL	3,270					
C	FOUNDATION						
1	CONCRETE LABOR/MATL	38,771	38,771	38,771	0	100%	TOP LINE CONCRETE
2	TERMITE TREATMENT	900					PERMATREAT
	TOTAL	39,671					
	TOTALS						

PAGE 1

Figure 5-2. Filled-in budget form for the first draw (Page 1 of 3).

39

CONSTRUCTION LOAN TRACKING SCHEDULE

Date: 25 SEPT
DRAW NUMBER: 1

Builder's Name: MICHAEL POMPEII
House Location: 24 IRONWOOD RD

Item #	Activity	Estimated Cost	Actual Cost for this Draw	Actual Cost to Date	Cost to Complete	Percent Complete	Contractor Name & Phone
D	MASONRY						
1	EXTERIOR BRICK	22,700					R. DYE JR. MASONRY
2	CONCRETE SIDEWALKS AND PATIO	4,500					TOP LINE CONCRETE
	TOTAL	27,200					
E	BUILDING MATERIALS + LABOR						
1	LUMBER MATL	43,350					CONTRACTOR YARD
2	FRAMING LABOR	28,000					JASPER CONSTRUCTION
3	FINISH CARPENTRY	16,500					CARSON GARLAND
4	ROOF	10,300					KEVIN'S ROOFING
5	WINDOWS	21,300					CONTRACTOR YARD
6	EXTERIOR DOORS	3,200					CONTRACTOR YARD
7	INTERIOR DOORS	5,800					CONTRACTOR YARD
	TOTAL	128,450					
F	PLUMB/ELEC/MECH						
1	PLUMBING LABOR + MATL	14,300					R+R PLUMBING
2	SEWER PUMP	6,500					PLIMCO, INC.
3	ELECTRIC MATL	3,700					OKESON ELECTRIC
4	ELECTRIC LABOR	8,000					OKESON ELECTRIC
5	MECHANICAL LABOR + MATL	18,100					CUSTOM DESIGN HVAC CO.
	TOTAL	50,600					
	TOTALS						

PAGE 2

Figure 5-2. Filled-in budget form for the first draw (Page 2 of 3).

CONSTRUCTION LOAN TRACKING SCHEDULE

Date: 25 SEPT
DRAW NUMBER: 1

Builder's Name: POMPEII
House Location: 24 IRONWOOD RD

Item #	Activity	Estimated Cost	Actual Cost for this Draw	Actual Cost to Date	Cost to Complete	Percent Complete	Contractor Name & Phone
G	INTERIOR WALLS/FLOORS						
1	INSULATION	7,600					S+K INSULATION
2	DRYWALL MATL + LABOR	12,600					ROCKY'S DRYWALL
3	PAINTING	10,200					RON POMPEII PAINTING INC
4	HARDWOOD FLOORS	11,400					RC LEES
5	HARDWOOD STAIRS	3,700					RC LEES
6	BATHROOM TILE	4,000					RC LEES
7	TILE FLOORING	1,500					RC LEES
8	CARPETING	13,700					RC LEES
	TOTAL	64,700					
H	EXTERIOR						
1	SIDING + TRIM PKG	10,200					RAY'S SIDING CO.
2	GUTTERS + DOWNSPOUTS	1,100					RAY'S SIDING CO.
3	REAR DECK LABOR/MATL	3,700					JASPER CONSTRUCTION
4	ASPHALT DRIVEWAY	13,800					GATOR PAVING
5	LANDSCAPING PKG	11,100					LIBERTY LANDSCAPING
	TOTAL	39,900					
I	MISCELLANEOUS						
1	KITCHEN CABINETS	16,500					NVR KITCHEN + BATH
2	KITCHEN COUNTERTOPS	6,200					"
3	KITCHEN APPLIANCES	4,300					"
4	BATHROOM VANITIES	2,100					
5	GARAGE DOOR SYSTEMS	2,300					AFFORDABLE DOOR CO.
6	FIXTURES, HARDWARE (ELEC.) (DOORS, CLOSETS)	6,500					VARIOUS
	TOTAL	37,900					
	TOTALS	405,379	46,701	46,701	358,678	11.5%	

PAGE 3

Figure 5-2. Filled-in budget form for the first draw (Page 3 of 3).

41

Figure 5-3 for you to copy and use, and a completed lien waiver is shown at Figure 5-4 as an example for you to follow. Your mortgage provider will probably have a very similar version for you to use.

11. Start construction.

12. After the completion of certain phases of the house construction, you need to pay your subcontractors in a timely manner (usually within 30 days). For example, once the excavation, footings, foundation walls, and concrete slabs are completed, submit the paperwork and receipts to the mortgage company for a "draw".

13. After receiving the paperwork and receipts, an inspector from the mortgage company will visit your site to make sure the work has been completed. If the inspection is satisfactory, the mortgage company will deposit the amount of money you requested into your checking account. The typical time for receiving this deposit is 3 to 5 days after you submit your paperwork.

14. With the money now in your checking account, pay the subcontractors whose work was completed.

15. Begin to make monthly payments on your construction loan, only for the cumulative amount of money that was put into your checking account. This monthly payment must be made during each month of construction, and will grow each month as your expenses add up and construction progresses.

WAIVER OF LIENS

The undersigned, being a party to the construction of certain improvements on real property located and described as follows (full legal description):

_____

_____

_____

_____

hereby acknowledges receipt of $ _____ for labor or materials provided by the undersigned as follows:

_____

_____

_____

(Specify with detail the labor and material provided, i.e., carpentry work for completion of first floor. If labor or material was provided to more than one (1) property, specify the labor or material for each property and the allocation of the payment.)

The undersigned does hereby waive, release and quit claim all right to a lien upon the land and improvements above described as a result of work done and/or materials furnished by the undersigned, any employees, materialmen and subcontractors through billing period for which this payment is made.

The undersigned warrants that all laborers and subcontractors employed in the performance of the work and all materialmen who have furnished materials and services have been fully paid; that none of such laborers, such subcontractors or such materialmen have asserted a claim against or a lien upon the premises hereinabove described; that no chattel mortgage, conditional bill of sale, or retention of title agreement has been executed or given with respect to any item or property used in conjunction with or incorporated into the improvements on the premises hereinabove described; that no claim has been assigned or will be assigned for payment or right to perfect a lien against said land and improvements; and that the undersigned is fully authorized and empowered to execute this waiver of liens.

The undersigned understands and agrees that the owner, any lender, and any title insurance company are entitled to rely upon this waiver.

WITNESS AND ATTEST

Company: _____

By: _____

Print Name/Title: _____

STATE OF _____

COUNTY OF _____

Subscribed, sworn to, and acknowledged before me this _____ day of _____, _____.

Notary Public: _____ My Commission Expires: _____

* NOTE: <u>Company name and title of person signing must appear above.</u>

Figure 5-3. Blank lien waiver form for you to copy and use.

WAIVER OF LIENS

The undersigned, being a party to the construction of certain improvements on real property located and described as follows (full legal description):

24 IRONWOOD ROAD

LOT 3 FITZHUGH SUBDIVISION

STAFFORD COUNTY VA

BUILDER: MICHAEL POMPEII

hereby acknowledges receipt of $ _2,366.84_ for labor or materials provided by the undersigned as follows:

BUILDING MATERIALS THROUGH ·2/25/03

(Specify with detail the labor and material provided, i.e., carpentry work for completion of first floor. If labor or material was provided to more than one (1) property, specify the labor or material for each property and the allocation of the payment.)

The undersigned does hereby waive, release and quit claim all right to a lien upon the land and improvements above described as a result of work done and/or materials furnished by the undersigned, any employees, materialmen and subcontractors through billing period for which this payment is made.

The undersigned warrants that all laborers and subcontractors employed in the performance of the work and all materialmen who have furnished materials and services have been fully paid; that none of such laborers, such subcontractors or such materialmen have asserted a claim against or a lien upon the premises hereinabove described; that no chattel mortgage, conditional bill of sale, or retention of title agreement has been executed or given with respect to any item or property used in conjunction with or incorporated into the improvements on the premises hereinabove described; that no claim has been assigned or will be assigned for payment or right to perfect a lien against said land and improvements; and that the undersigned is fully authorized and empowered to execute this waiver of liens.

The undersigned understands and agrees that the owner, any lender, and any title insurance company are entitled to rely upon this waiver.

WITNESS AND ATTEST

Company: _THE CONTRACTOR YARD INC._

By: _James GMcGinniss Jr_

Print Name/Title: _James G McGinniss Jr._

STATE OF _Virginia_

COUNTY OF _Spotsylvania_

Subscribed, sworn to, and acknowledged before me this _10_ day of _March_, _2003_.

Notary Public: _Melanie D Taylor_ My Commission Expires: _February 28, 2006_

* NOTE: <u>Company name and title of person signing must appear above</u>.

Figure 5-4. An example of a filled-in lien waiver.

16. Repeat the draw process after each phase of house construction. It is typical to have between 5 and 8 separate draws in the construction loan. For example:

    a. Draw #1 may be made after completion of the foundation.

    b. Draw #2 after the framing is complete.

    c. Draw #3 after the roofing and siding are complete.

    d. Draw #4 after the rough-in mechanical, plumbing, and electrical is complete.

    e. Draw #5 after the drywall, interior trim, and initial painting is complete.

    f. Draw #6 after the kitchen, bathroom, and flooring is complete.

    g. Draw #7 after the finish mechanical, plumbing, and electrical, and carpet is complete.

    h. Draw #8 after landscaping, driveway, and all other finish work is complete.

17. In order to receive the last draw, you must pass a final inspection by the mortgage company, have all lien waivers signed, and an "occupancy permit" must be issued (if required by your local city or county government).

18. Your construction loan is now completed, and the construction loan must now be transferred or "rolled over" to a mortgage loan. This is done at your attorney's office. If you have a construction-perm loan, the process is very simple with a minimum of paperwork and fees. If you did not use a construction-perm loan, then you must go through the entire loan process again to get your mortgage.

19. Once the mortgage loan has paid off the construction loan, you begin making monthly payments on your permanent mortgage loan.

20. The construction loan process is now finished.

This whole construction loan process may seem quite complicated, but don't worry. A good mortgage company and a good attorney will be doing most of the work and guiding you every step of the way. All you need to do is to take it one step at a time, let the mortgage company do their job, and it will come out just fine in the end. It did for me.

5.3 INSURANCE

Insurance against theft, fire, vandalism, or other types of loss for the house you are building is absolutely essential. Any licensed insurance agent or company that sells homeowner's insurance can probably provide you with builder's insurance. You simply call the insurance agent, ask for builder's insurance, provide a starting date for construction, tell them the estimated value of your new finished home, make a payment, and get a policy issued to you. Some insurance companies may differ, but that's all I had to do.

Here is how my builder's insurance policy worked for me, and yours will probably be very similar:

a) From day one, the policy amount is based on the total cost of the finished house, no matter how far along you are during construction.

b) The cost of the builder's insurance is the same amount that you would pay if you were already living in the new house and had the same homeowner's policy and coverage.

c) Theft at the new building site is not covered unless the new house is closed in and the stolen items were locked up inside the house.

d) You will not be able to obtain a construction loan until your builder's insurance policy is paid for and in effect. Your insurance company will probably have to send a certificate of insurance to your bank or mortgage company.

Overall, getting insurance is one of the easier things to get done when you are building your house because all it involves is a simple phone call. Remember, your insurance agent is an expert at what he or she does, so let them do their job to make your homebuilding experience that much easier.

Chapter 6

PLANNING AND SCHEDULING

Another critical element that will determine your success in building your home is your degree of preparation. Preparation means thinking ahead, making plans and contingencies, constantly developing and refining plans and schedules, and following through on the plans and schedules in a timely manner. Simply put, the quality of your house planning and scheduling efforts and the amount time you spend on them will have a direct and significant impact on your success!

6.1 TYPES OF SCHEDULES

The key to good planning for the construction of your new house is to develop and maintain realistic schedules. During the process of building my house, I found that only two types of schedules were necessary. The first is a preliminary "Monthly Schedule" and the second is a detailed "Weekly Schedule".

The Monthly Schedule is developed and used mainly BEFORE any construction begins, and is used to plan for and establish a basic rough schedule for your new house construction. The Weekly Schedule is also initially developed before construction, but it is much more specific and will be heavily used and constantly refined during the entire construction process.

6.2 MONTHLY SCHEDULE

You need to start the planning process by developing your own Monthly Schedule. This schedule is somewhat easy to develop because it is very general in nature and does not get into any specific detail on any part of the construction process. It is just used as a general planning document to let you know what should be happening each month, and will serve as a guide in developing your more detailed weekly schedule. Figure 6.1 shows an example of the Monthly Schedule that I used for my house.

In addition, a blank Monthly Schedule is shown in Figure 6.2 for you to use in developing your own Monthly Schedule. Just make copies of Figure 6.2 and write in your best guess of your major monthly activities, using Figure 6.1 as a guide. Your monthly schedule will vary and will depend on the size and complexity of your new house.

You may believe that some activities may take less time, more time, or may overlap several months. This is fine, so just use your best estimate. Keep in mind that different areas of the country may have slightly different construction methods, customs, schedules, and weather related delays. For example, if you live in the northern U.S. and your outside construction falls during the winter months, you can just about guarantee that there will be significant construction delays due to snow and cold weather. You do not have to be perfect with the Monthly Schedule; just be as realistic as you can.

MONTHLY SCHEDULE   Date: __15 APRIL__   Page #: __1__

Month/Year	Activity
MAY 03	- DEVELOP HOUSE REQUIREMENTS LIST - SELECT & MODIFY HOUSE PLAN - PURCHASE LAND
JUNE 03	- PERFORM COST ESTIMATES - APPLY FOR CONSTRUCTION LOAN - APPLY FOR BUILDING PERMIT
JULY 03	- LINE UP SUBCONTRACTORS - CLOSE ON CONSTRUCTION LOAN - CLEAR LAND - RECEIVE BUILDING PERMIT
AUG 03	- EXCAVATE DRIVEWAY & BASEMENT - POUR FOOTERS & BASEMENT WALLS - UNDER SLAB PLUMBING - ORDER LONG LEAD ITEMS - POUR BASEMENT & GARAGE SLABS
SEP 03	- FRAMING
OCT 03	- ROOFING - WINDOWS & DOORS - BRICK - HVAC & PLUMBING ROUGH-IN

Figure 6-1. An example of a filled-in Monthly Schedue (page 1 of 2).

MONTHLY SCHEDULE   Date: _15 APRIL_   Page #: _2_

Month/Year	Activity
NOV 03	- SIDING, TRIM, & GUTTERS - WATER & SEWER LINES - ELECTRICAL ROUGH-IN - CONCRETE PATIO & SIDEWALKS
DEC 03	- INSULATION - DRYWALL
JAN 04	- INTERIOR TRIM & DOORS - PRIMER PAINT
FEB 04	- INSTALL KITCHEN & BATHS - GARAGE DOORS - PAINTING
MAR 04	- FINISH PLUMBING, HVAC, ELECTRICAL - HARDWOOD, TILE, VINYL FLOORING
APR 04	- DOOR, CLOSET, BATH HARDWARE - CARPETING - FINAL PAINTING & CLEANING - LANDSCAPING & DRIVEWAY - MOVE-IN

Figure 6-1. An example of a filled-in Monthly Schedue (page 2 of 2).

MONTHLY SCHEDULE

Date: _____   *Page #:* _____

Month/Year	Activity

Figure 6-2. Blank monthly schedule for you to copy and use.

6.3 WEEKLY SCHEDULE

Using the monthly schedule that you just developed as a guide, you can now develop the first draft of your own Weekly Schedule. I call this the first draft because your Weekly Schedule will be constantly refined and updated as you get new information on weather delays, early or late material deliveries, subcontractor availabilities and schedule changes, or a whole host of other reasons specific to your own situation. THE WEEKLY SCHEDULE IS THE MOST IMPORTANT AND MOST USED SCHEDULE. You will find yourself referring to this weekly schedule on almost a daily basis.

As an example for you, Figure 6-3 shows one of the weekly schedules that I used for my house. Note that I used a handwritten schedule instead of a fancier, computer software generated schedule. I am very computer literate, and I tried using several versions of fancy scheduling software, but I quickly found out that I was spending an excessive amount of time trying to get the software to do what I wanted it to do. My time was better spent trying to figure out my weekly schedule, rather that spending most of my time trying to figure out the software. Unless you are a true expert at using scheduling software, I recommend that you just use my simple handwritten Weekly Schedule. It is simple, fast, and easy to do.

In addition, a blank Weekly Schedule is shown in Figure 6-4 for you to use in developing your own Weekly Schedule. Just make copies of Figure 6-4 and write in your specific weekly activities, using the sample schedule at Figure 6-3 as a guide. For your first Weekly Schedule, you do not need to be perfectly accurate with everything, so don't worry. Just get it as close as you can with the information that you have. As you acquire more information on subcontractors and their schedules, material delivery schedules, and weather conditions, you can always easily update and refine your Weekly Schedule.

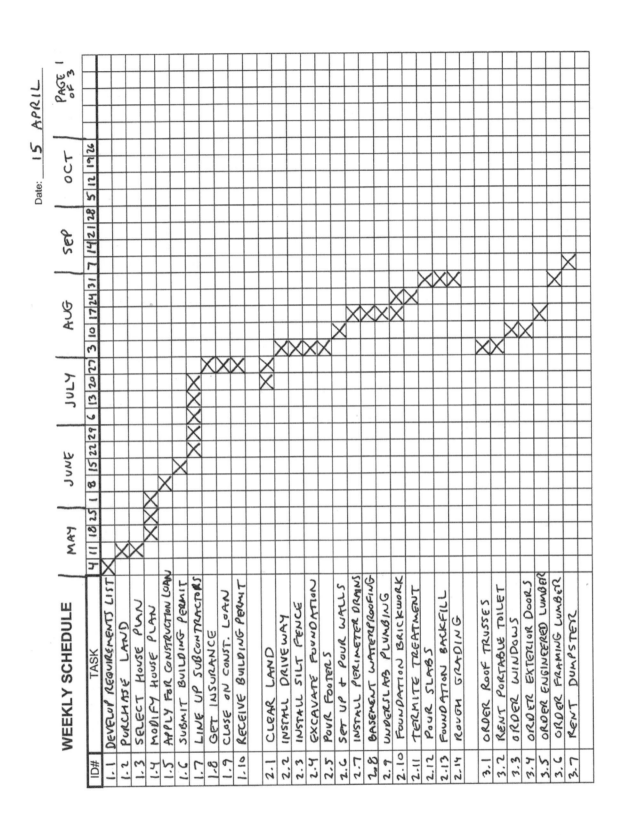

Figure 6-3. An example of a filled-in Weekly Schedue (page 1 of 3).

55

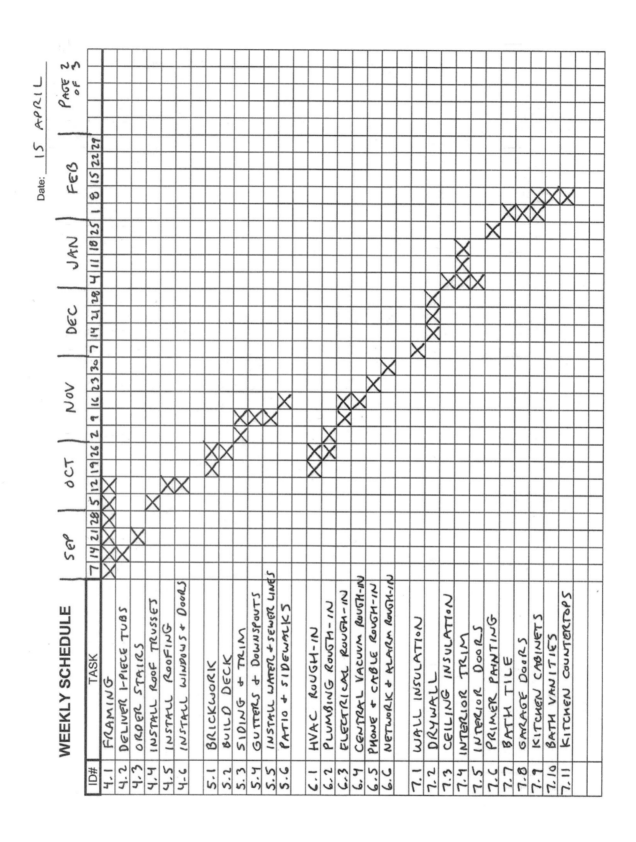

Figure 6-3. An example of a filled-in Weekly Schedue (page 2 of 3).

56

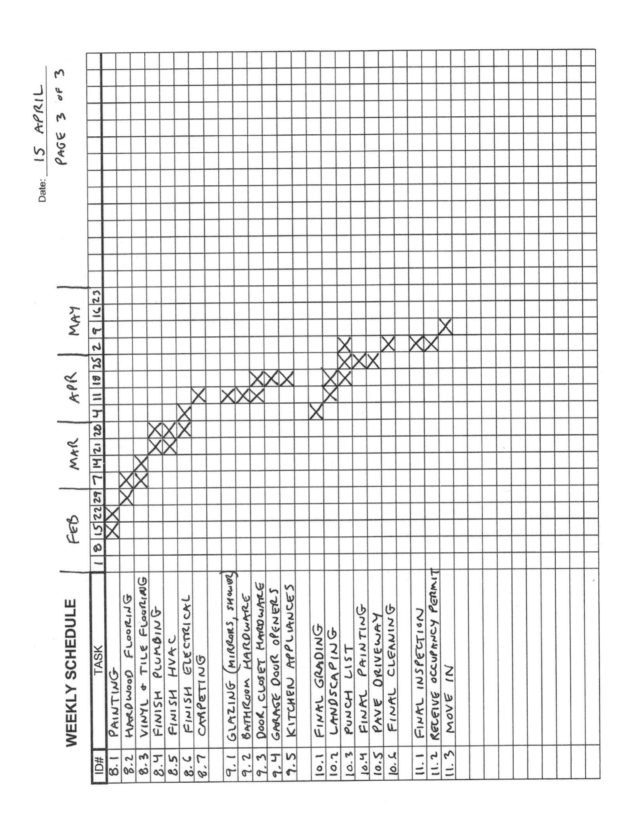

Figure 6-3. An example of a filled-in Weekly Schedue (page 3 of 3).

57

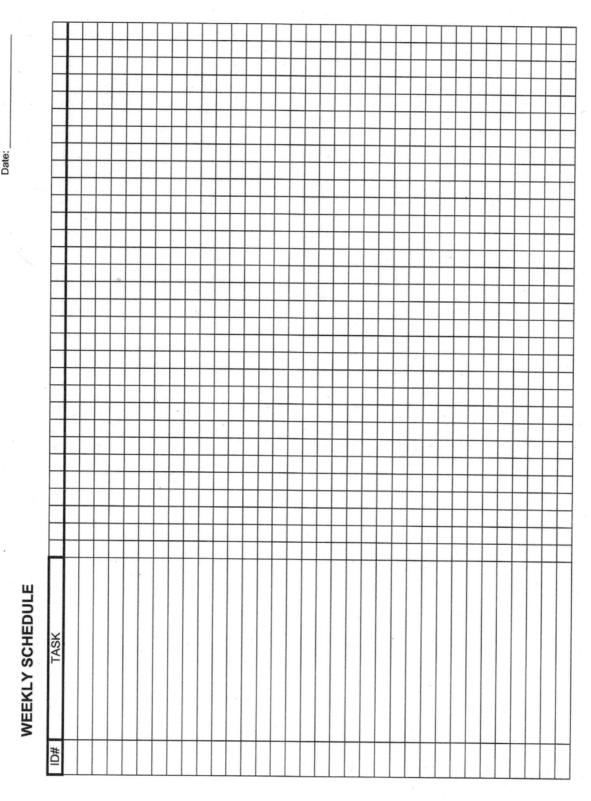

Figure 6-4. Blank Weekly Schedule for you to copy and use.

58

IMPORTANT: It is imperative that you take the time to update this schedule frequently, perhaps as often as every week or two during construction.

As previously mentioned, you will find that this Weekly Schedule is the single most important tool in efficiently and effectively building your house. This is because it is always there to guide you on who you have to call next, what you have to order next, and what actions you have to take next. As busy as you will be during the construction, you will absolutely need all the help you can get, and your Weekly Schedule will turn out to be an indispensable tool!

6.4 LONG LEAD ITEMS

Now is the time to make a list of special items that take a long time to be manufactured and/or delivered. These are commonly referred to as "long lead items". Typical long lead items consist of special order windows of various sizes and quantities, exterior doors, prefabricated roof trusses, steel beams used for beams and girders, prefabricated or custom stair systems, decorative support columns, and special decorative trim pieces.

Carefully review your construction drawings and house plans, and carefully develop a list of any long lead items that you will require. Remember, you do not want your entire construction project held up for weeks or months because you forgot to order something that takes weeks or months to deliver. Call the various supplies and inquire about their typical lead times for your items. Then add this information into your Weekly Schedule to cue you on when you need to place your orders.

It is wise to give yourself a few weeks of cushion to make up for any possible manufacturing or delivery delays, but not too much. For example, you do not want $20,000 worth of windows sitting on the job site for 3 or 4 weeks before they are needed. You want the windows delivered just before they will be installed to minimize the chance of theft or breakage by other subcontractors or vandals. This is yet another reason why your Weekly Schedule is so important.

6.5 ESSENTIAL TOOLS AND EQUIPMENT

The final stage of pre-construction preparation is assembling the tools and equipment that you, the general contractor, will need during construction. The following list of items will be essential, so you might as well go ahead and begin looking into and/or purchasing them now. Here is the list:

1. <u>Large trash dumpster</u>. These can be rented from a local waste management company. They usually come in 20- and 30-cubic yard sizes, and you can expect to pay a drop off fee, a monthly rental fee, a pickup fee, and a disposal fee (by the ton) each time it is emptied. My advice is to go with the largest size because you will save money in the long run by paying less in drop off and pickup fees, plus you will welcome the less frequent calls to the trash company in arranging pickups. To save money, do not have the dumpster dropped off until the framing stage is under way. Make sure the dumpster is placed fairly close to the house, but not close enough to interfere with ladders, scaffolding, or any foundation backfilling that needs to be done. If your local city or county allows, you can also save money by burning any clean, combustible materials on site, since the disposal fee is paid on a per ton basis, and you will need less frequent pickups because there will be more room available in the dumpster. Just do not burn any materials that may emit toxic fumes, such as styrofoam products or vinyl siding and trim.

2. <u>Portable toilet</u>. These are also called "porta-potties" and can be rented on a monthly basis. They also typically come with a cleaning service every two

weeks. Don't even think about not renting one, because you and your subcontractors will be grateful that it is there when you need it. Remember, happy and comfortable subcontractors will do better work for you. Also, make sure that the portable toilet is placed in a location where it can be easily serviced by a heavy truck that does not have to travel through possible muddy conditions. If it is muddy, they will not service the toilet. I made the mistake of placing the portable toilet in the rear corner of my lot during dry conditions, only to have it rain and have the ensuing mud prevent the service truck from cleaning it out for several months.

3. <u>Portable electric generator</u>. You will need this to run pumps, lights, power tools, and shop vacuum until you can get temporary or permanent electricity installed. A generator in the range of 2500 to 3000 watts may be your best bet.

4. <u>Shop vacuum</u>. You will be using this a lot when you are constantly cleaning up after your subcontractors, so get a good one. To save yourself time, make sure it has high power, is high quality, and has a wet/dry capability.

5. <u>Electric sump pump</u>. This is a small electric pump used for pumping rainwater from floors, basements, and ditches. They use a common garden hose for discharge, and a decent one will cost in the $50 to $75 range.

6. <u>6-foot stepladder</u>. This must be sturdy and high quality because you will be using it a lot.

7. <u>16-foot extension ladder</u>. This ladder will be used to reach places that your 6-foot stepladder cannot. It is actually about 8-feet long when retracted, and can extend to a working length of about 13 feet. A lightweight ladder works well here.

8. <u>Basic cleaning supplies</u>. You will probably use these items so much that you will wear them out. This includes: 1) a high quality push broom with bristles made for sweeping semi-smooth floors, 2) a regular broom for reaching in corners and other places where the push broom will not fit, 3) a good dustpan, and 4) a large trash can that you can carry or wheel around while full. For the trash can, a sturdy 40 to 50 gallon plastic trash container works well.

9. <u>Good high top boots</u>. These are a necessity because of all the wood, nails, concrete, and mud you will be walking around on. Get a pair with steel toes, because it will probably save you some hurt toes at one time or another. Also, make sure that the boots have soles where mud can be easily cleaned off; it will save you a lot of time, hassle, and cleaning in the house. Don't get boots with deep treads that will hold mud. Boots that are easy to put on and take off will also end up being a welcome feature.

10. <u>Basic power tools</u>. This includes a good circular saw with a carbide tipped blade, a good electric drill, and a high quality and powerful cordless drill with at least two battery packs. Make sure you get some high quality drill bits ranging from 1/32 inch to about 3/8 inch; you will use these a lot.

11. <u>Basic hand tools</u>. These are the common tools that you probably already have, and include a good 25-foot tape measure, screwdrivers, hammer, pliers, crow bar, framing square, a small 6-inch level, a larger 3- or 4-foot level, shovel, small hand shovel, and a good tool box to keep things organized.

12. <u>Miscellaneous hardware</u>. This includes a wide variety of nails, screws, bolts, and other hardware. You will be surprised by the number of trips you will make to the hardware store, and you will accumulate and use almost every type and size of nails and screws.

13. <u>Truck</u>. I had a small pickup truck, and it proved to be very valuable for hauling building supplies, lumber, and trash. If you do not own a pickup truck, you may want to purchase a used truck and keep it at least from the time you start construction until about two months after you move in. You will be glad you did.

Chapter 7

PERMITS, BUILDING CODES, AND INSPECTIONS

7.1 PERMITS

Most cities or counties will not allow you to build your house unless they approve the type of construction, the construction details, and the location of the construction on your lot. This approval comes through the issuing of a *building permit*.

The first thing you need to do is to call your local government offices to find out if a permit is required. The specific department may be named Building Administration, Code Administration, Building Department, or something similar. If a permit is required, ask them to send you a building permit application and information package. Also, make sure that they send you a list of fees. There will probably be fees for the permit, fees for the drawing review, fees for inspections, erosion bonds, and various taxes. The people in the building department will be happy to explain any requirements or fees that are confusing or may not be clear. If your locality does not require building permits, then you can skip this step.

A typical application package that you will need to submit for a building permit will probably consist of a one or two page application form, a complete set of drawings, and a survey plat that shows the location of the house on the lot. You will also have to pay the building permit fees, which are usually based on the square footage of your proposed house.

A note of caution: Make sure that you find out the amount of time it will take for your application to be approved and the building permit issued. Depending on where you live, this time period could be days, weeks, or it even could be many months. The construction of my house was delayed for two months because it took my county three full months to review my application package and issue my permit!

7.2 BUILDING CODES

A major reason that localities require building permits (besides the money) is to ensure that your new construction will meet all current building codes. Building codes are standards of construction that must be used to ensure that your new house is safe, sturdy, habitable, and up to date with the latest building technologies, materials, and equipment. These codes cover areas such as structural (foundation, framing, floors, walls, roof), plumbing, electrical, mechanical, stairs and railings, insulation, fire related issues, heating and cooling efficiency, and safety.

There are several building codes used throughout the U.S. and internationally, and each one of these codes is generally similar. The building code that is enforced by your locality will mostly depend on what area of the country you live in. For residential construction, most areas have adopted one of the three most widely used codes:

66

(1) International One and Two Family Dwelling Code, published by the International Conference of Building Officials (ICBO),

(2) National Building Code, published by the Building Officials and Code Administrators (BOCA),

(3) Standard Building Code, published by the Southern Building Code Congress International (SBCCI).

As the general contractor for your new house construction, you need to be aware of your local building codes, but you do not need to be an all-knowing expert in all code requirements. Leave this detailed knowledge of codes up to your subcontractors and local government inspectors. Codes are constantly being changed and updated, and your subcontractors work within these codes on a daily basis. For example, any reputable and licensed electrician will know what wire sizes, connection types, outlet locations, and circuit breaker sizes need to go into your house to meet or exceed the electrical codes. The same goes for your other subcontractors. But be aware that some code language may be subject to different interpretations, and situations will vary from house to house. In this case, your local inspector and/or the head building official in your locality will have the final word on any controversial issues.

7.3 INSPECTIONS

When your city or county issues you a building permit, they need some way of ensuring that you build according to your approved drawings, and that all construction is done according to the building codes. The locality will ensure this compliance by performing periodic inspections of your construction in progress.

The type and quantity of inspections will vary by locality. Some localities will perform dozens of inspections over the entire course of construction, while others with limited staffs may only perform a few inspections. As an example, here is a list of inspections that had to be performed and passed for my new house:

(1) First Erosion

(2) Concrete Footing

(3) Backfill/Waterproofing

(4) Poured Concrete Wall

(5) Concrete Footing (Deck Piers)

(6) Plumbing Groundwork

(7) Concrete Slab (Basement and Garage)

(8) Plumbing Rough-In

(9) Mechanical Rough-In

(10) Electrical Rough-In

(11) Mechanical, Gas Line

(12) Fireplace, Gas

(13) Electrical, Permanent Meter

(14) Framing

(15) Insulation

(16) Energy Efficiency (Windows, Doors, Hot Water, Furnace, Cooling)

(17) Final Inspection

During the construction process, you will not be able to legally proceed with your construction until each phase has successfully passed its inspection. For example, you will not be able to install insulation until the rough-in plumbing, electrical, and heating/cooling systems have passed their inspections. Then you will not be able to put up drywall until the insulation has passed its inspection, and so on.

When your construction reaches a point that is ready for a certain inspection, you simply call the building department to schedule the inspection. If you are lucky, the inspector will come the next day. It is a good idea to be at the site during the inspection so that the inspector can point out any problem areas to you in person. You will find that some inspectors may be very detailed and nit-picky, while others will take a general look and be done in a few minutes.

If the inspector does point out problems and fails an inspection on your house, do not get defensive or be argumentative. The inspector is only doing his or her job, and fixing any problems will be better and safer for you and your family in the long run. So always try to be courteous and respectful toward the inspector. It will pay off in your future inspections!

When the building inspector comes to your new home and performs an inspection, the inspector will usually leave a filled-out inspection sheet posted on a door or window that shows if the inspection was passed or not. The inspection sheet that my building inspector used for my final inspection is shown in Figure 7-1. Your local inspector will probably use something similar.

The final inspection is perhaps the most important inspection, as it will result in the issuing of an Occupancy Permit (or sometimes called a Certificate of Occupancy). Successfully passing this final inspection will require that all other inspections have been passed and that there are no other outstanding code or building violations. Your lender will require a copy of this Occupancy Permit to close out your construction loan and to process your mortgage, and this will now allow you to legally move into your new home.

Residential Permit Inspection Codes:
STAFFORD COUNTY
Dept. of Code Administration

Permit # 2 2 3 3 / 0   Date 4/15/03

Lot # 3   658-8650 For Info.

Type of Inspection	Approved	Rejected
100 EROSION, FIRST/STEEP SLOPE		
199 EROSION, FINAL		
200 FOOTING		
201 FOOTING/JOINT FOUNDATION		
202 BACKFILL/WATERPROOFING		
203 POURED WALL		
204 SLAB		
212 FOUNDATION		
300 PLUMBING/ROUGH-IN		
301 PLUMBING/GROUNDWORKS		
302 PLUMBING/WATER LINE		
303 PLUMBING/SEWER LINE		
400 MECHANICAL/ROUGH-IN		
401 MECHANICAL/GAS LINE/INSIDE		
402 MECHANICAL/TANKS/PROPANE/OIL		
403 MECHANICAL/GAS LINE/OUTSIDE		
405 WOODSTOVE/INSERT/THIMBLE		
408 FIREPLACE/PREFAB/RELINE		
409 HEARTH		
411 THROAT		
500 ELECTRIC/ROUGH-IN		
501 ELECTRIC METER		
502 ELECTRIC/STEEL & BONDING		
505 TEMPORARY ELECTRIC METER		
600 FRAMING		
601 ENERGY		
602 INSULATION		
603 SOUND TRANSMISSION/APT.		
604 SOUND TRANSMISSION/AIRPORT		
799 FINAL/ZONING		
999 FINAL	R7√	
950 OTHER		

**THIS INSPECTION VERIFICATION MUST BE
POSTED UNTIL THE FINAL INSPECTION**
DO NOT REMOVE
FOR INSPECTIONS CALL: (540) 658-4151

Figure 7-1. Typical Inspection Sheet that the inspector will leave to show if an inspection was passed or not.

Chapter 8

SELECTING AND WORKING WITH SUBCONTRACTORS

8.1 SELECTING SUBCONTRACTORS

As already mentioned several times in this book, your subcontractors are your hired experts that will be working for you in their own specific area of expertise. Each subcontractor will use their own specific knowledge, skills, and experience for completing their work in a timely manner with a minimum of problems or issues for you or them. A good subcontractor will know the best way to get things done because they know their materials, know the local building codes and know what installation processes work and which ones do not.

There are many factors to consider when deciding on who to hire as your subcontractors. Licensing may be the most important factor, so make sure that whoever you hire is licensed in your state, especially with plumbing, electrical, and mechanical subcontractors. Going with the lowest bidder may not always be the best way to go, and could possibly cost more and cause more headaches in the long run. Perhaps the best way to find a good, reliable subcontractor is by word of mouth. Ask around with friends, coworkers, and possibly some specialized building supply stores (plumbing suppliers, electrical suppliers, masonry suppliers, lumberyards, etc.) to find out who does a good job and who is reliable.

Reliability is important because you will probably find that your biggest problem will be getting certain subcontractors to show up when they are supposed to. Many subcontractors may be over-committed or may have to go off on bigger jobs for the big builders that they rely on for most of their work. If you live in an area where there is a housing boom, it may be even more difficult to get good subcontractors to come and work for you.

But this was not the case for me. The house that I was building was in one of the fastest growing counties in the United States, and building subcontractors were stretched very thin. I only had problems with one subcontractor (brickwork) not showing up when he was supposed to, and this caused considerable reworking of my weekly schedule and minor rescheduling of some other subcontractors. But overall, I was genuinely pleased with the reliability, dependability, and workmanship of almost all of the subcontractors that I hired. This was due to the process that I used for hiring my subcontractors, and this process will probably work for you, too.

When looking for any particular subcontractor, here is the 10-step process that I used and that I recommend that you use for selecting your subcontractors:

MY TEN STEP PROCESS FOR CHOOSING A SUBCONTRACTOR

1) Ask for referrals from friends, co-workers, or trade-specific suppliers.

2) If you receive no referrals for a particular subcontractor, search the ads in newspapers and yellow pages.

72

3) Make phone calls to two or three prospective subcontractors.

4) If you have to leave a message and they do not return your call within a day or two, cross them off your list! This is a good indicator that they will not return your calls if you hire them.

5) Explain to them what you are doing, the type of work you are looking for, ask if they are licensed, and ask what they have to offer.

6) If you are happy with their response, ask if you can meet with them to go over drawings and to get a bid on the job. If you do not get a good feeling with their response, then just thank them for their time and tell them that you need to look at some other options. ALWAYS REMEMBER TO GO WITH YOUR GUT FEELING. If you don't get a good feeling about doing business with that subcontractor, then you will usually be right!

7) When you go to meet with them to go over drawings and to get a cost estimate (or bid), ask about any recent jobs they have done, and ask about lead times that they would need to show up at your building site.

8) During this meeting with the subcontractor, listen carefully to everything they say and be a judge their competence, character, and integrity. Integrity is defined in Webster's Dictionary as "rigid adherence to a code or standard of values". If you sense that integrity is important to the subcontractor, then you will most likely be getting a subcontractor that will be reliable, dependable, and do good work for you.

9) Meet with and get cost estimates from at least two subcontractors.

10) Armed with information on cost, integrity, and your gut feeling, choose the subcontractor.

This process worked very well for me, so it will probably work very well for you, too. Use it ---- it works!

8.2 COMBINING SUBCONTRACTORS

A listing of jobs that you may need to have subcontracted is shown in Figure 8-1. But don't let the large number of jobs frighten you, as many of these jobs can be combined. In fact, it is much to your advantage to combine the jobs of as many of these subcontractors as you can. You will end up having less people to call and coordinate, less paperwork, less workers at the home site, less bills to pay, and less issues and hassles. In addition, this provides an incentive for the subcontractor to show up at the right time and get the work completed on time because the subcontractor now has a larger job and will be getting more money. Here are some examples of subcontractors that can be combined to make things much easier for you to coordinate and manage:

1) DRIVEWAY, EXCAVATION, FOUNDATION, and CONCRETE: This turned out to be one of the greatest time saving and cost saving combinations in my home building process. I found a reputable concrete company that also provided excavation services, and I negotiated an entire package of work with this single company. The work package included the following: a) install culvert piping, b) grade and install gravel driveway, c) excavate for the foundation, d) install concrete footers, e) install poured concrete walls, f) install exterior foundation waterproofing, g) install external perimeter drainage system, h) backfill foundation to the rough grade, i) install interior perimeter drainage system, j) install basement slab gravel, k) pour basement concrete slab, l) backfill garage floor and

74

FIGURE 8-1. LISTING OF SUBCONTRACTORS THAT YOU MAY NEED.

- ❑ Design and drafting
- ❑ Construction loan
- ❑ Appraiser
- ❑ Surveyor
- ❑ Insurance
- ❑ Land clearing
- ❑ Erosion control
- ❑ Driveway grading and gravel
- ❑ Excavation
- ❑ Concrete footers
- ❑ Foundation walls
- ❑ Foundation drainage
- ❑ Foundation waterproofing
- ❑ Brickwork
- ❑ Underground plumbing
- ❑ Termite treatment
- ❑ Basement and garage slabs
- ❑ Exterior water supply line
- ❑ Exterior sewer line / septic
- ❑ Electrical service
- ❑ Natural gas service
- ❑ Telephone service
- ❑ Cable TV service
- ❑ Backfill foundation
- ❑ Rough grade
- ❑ Lumber
- ❑ Engineered lumber design
- ❑ Steel beam design
- ❑ Roof truss supplier
- ❑ Doors, Windows
- ❑ Building supplies
- ❑ Portable toilet
- ❑ Trash dumpster
- ❑ Framing
- ❑ Stair design
- ❑ HVAC system design
- ❑ Rough in mechanical/HVAC
- ❑ Rough in plumbing
- ❑ Rough in electrical
- ❑ Insulation

- ❑ Siding
- ❑ Exterior Trim
- ❑ Gutters and downspouts
- ❑ Deck
- ❑ Patio
- ❑ Sidewalks
- ❑ Drywall hanging
- ❑ Drywall finishing
- ❑ Interior trim and doors
- ❑ Primer painting
- ❑ Kitchen cabinets
- ❑ Kitchen countertops
- ❑ Bathroom vanities
- ❑ Bathroom tile
- ❑ Painting
- ❑ Hardwood flooring
- ❑ Vinyl flooring
- ❑ Tile flooring
- ❑ Carpeting
- ❑ Bathroom fixture supplier
- ❑ Finish plumbing
- ❑ Electrical fixture supplier
- ❑ Finish plumbing
- ❑ Finish mechanical/HVAC
- ❑ Garage doors
- ❑ Garage door openers
- ❑ Glazing (mirrors, shower doors, etc.)
- ❑ Door hardware
- ❑ Closet hardware
- ❑ Bathroom hardware
- ❑ Kitchen appliances
- ❑ Final painting
- ❑ Final grading
- ❑ Landscaping
- ❑ Asphalt/concrete driveway
- ❑ Final cleaning
- ❑ Punch list
- ❑ Final inspection
- ❑ Moving company

add gravel, m) pour garage concrete slab, n) grade and install concrete patio slab, o) grade and install all concrete sidewalks, and p) install footers for deck supports. So I ended up combining about 5 or 6 different subcontractors into just one, and I basically got almost everything done to be ready for the framing subcontractor! I not only got a quality job done quickly, but also saved money by negotiating an entire package.

2) PLUMBING, EXTERIOR WATER AND SEWER LINES, and HOOKUP: Some plumbing companies only do interior or exterior plumbing work, but I found a good one that not only did all my interior supply and waste plumbing, but also dug, installed, and hooked up my outside water supply and sewer lines.

3) DRYWALL and PAINTING: There are some subcontractors that can hang drywall, finish the drywall, and take care of all painting. For my house, I went with separate subcontractors for these jobs because my cousin was a professional painter and provided me with an excellent deal.

4) KITCHEN and BATH: The same company that supplies and installs your kitchen cabinets and countertops can also supply and install your bathroom vanities and vanity tops.

5) HARDWOOD FLOORING, VINYL FLOORING, TILE FLOORING, BATHROOM TILE, and CARPETING: I negotiated a package deal with a store that supplied all flooring, tile, and carpeting that I needed. Again, this package deal not only saved me a lot of money, but eliminated many hassles from my hectic schedule.

6) ROOFING, SIDING, EXTERIOR TRIM, and GUTTERS: Many companies perform all of this work, and may be able to save you money on a package deal. For my house, I could not get the schedule to work out, so I hired

one company to do the roofing, and another company to do the vinyl siding, trim work, and gutters/downspouts as a package.

7) BUILDING SUPPLIES, LUMBER, DOORS, WINDOWS: This is one area that you definitely need to combine. This company proved to be the most important subcontractor in my entire home building process, and is discussed in detail in the next section.

8.3 THE MOST IMPORTANT SUBCONTRACTOR

I unexpectedly found that the most important thing you can do is to FIND A GOOD SALEPERSON AT A BUILDING SUPPLY STORE THAT CATERS SPECIFICALLY TO BUILDERS. Why? Because a good salesperson who knows the business, has access to any materials you need, can provide free flooring, header, truss, and stair design services, is always just a phone call away, and can deliver just about anything in a day or two to your home site IS WORTH THEIR WEIGHT IN GOLD. The time and money you save, plus the hassles and headaches you will avoid, will no doubt make your personal salesperson your most important subcontractor, too.

Here is what I did for my new house, and I highly recommend that you do something very similar.   Before I even started construction, I asked around for referrals on building suppliers in my area and who among them had the best prices and service. Several knowledgeable people pointed my to a store called The Contractor Yard, which is a division of the large Lowe's home improvement stores that are located across the country. The Contractor Yard only catered to builders, and they will not sell you anything unless you are a builder and you have an account with them. So I told them I was building my own house (which qualified me as a builder) and I signed up for an account with them. Am I glad I did!

I was immediately assigned a salesperson who would always be assisting me, and his name was Ronnie. Ronnie sat down with me, looked through my house plans and schedule, and quickly and efficiently told me what his store had to offer. I would not only get lumber, doors, windows, tools, nails, and just about any other supplies at a price cheaper than any home improvement store (and I checked), but I would also get free engineering design services of my engineered floor system, support beams and headers, engineered trusses, and custom prefabricated stairing. All I had to do was purchase the materials from that store (which were cheaper than a non-builder could buy). In addition, I could just call Ronnie on any day to order a large or small amount of lumber or building materials, and they would be delivered to my home site, free of charge, in one or two days. How can you beat that?

I ended up buying all of my lumber, engineered floor joists, engineered support beams, floor panels, wall panels, windows, exterior doors, interior doors, interior trim, and numerous other items from Ronnie. All I had to do was pick up the phone, tell him what I needed (he was always there everyday and returned my calls immediately if he was busy), and the correct supplies showed up where they were supposed to and when they were supposed to. No waste, no hassles. I even had it set up where my framing subcontractor could call Ronnie and have any needed materials delivered to my home site without me even being involved. I always got the invoices at the end of the month to verify all the supplies, and everything was always correct.

You probably get the point now about how valuable your building supply salesperson will be. Most cities and towns have building supply stores or lumberyards that cater to builders, and it is imperative to your home building experience to seek out and find a good salesperson to help you.

8.4 CONTRACTS AND PROPOSALS

Contract agreements with subcontractors are good but may not be practical. This is because most subcontractors want to use their own simple proposal forms. I have read other books on subcontracting, and most of them say to use fancy legal forms and contracts that spell out exactly what will be done in great detail, what it will cost, and a bunch of complicated legal statements that help to protect you. These types of legal agreements do help to protect you, and it is wise to use them, but what I found out is that they are just not practical in the real world.

I am telling you that there are very few subcontractors out there that will want to try to decipher some legal form that you ask them to sign. These subcontractors are mostly blue-collar workers who do not have a team of lawyers sitting back in their office ready to figure out if they should sign it or not. Instead, the subcontractor will typically provide you with a simple proposal form that lists, in very basic terms, what they propose to do and what it will cost. That is the "contract" that you will most likely end up signing, if you sign anything at all. If you insist on using a complicated legal contract, many subcontractors will just not want to deal with you.

Lawyers out there are probably somewhat upset over what I just said, but that's just the way it is in my part of the country. Your part of the country may be different, but it is most likely the same. Therefore, please read the next section very carefully, as it may be one of the most important lessons in this book:

IMPORTANT - IMPORTANT - IMPORTANT

You can greatly lessen your risk of a subcontractor ripping you off by: 1) using the selection criteria in section 8.1, 2) by not paying the subcontractor anything up front, 3) by paying the subcontractor only for the work that has been completed to date, and 4) by using the final payment criteria in section 8.5.

Please note that there may be some cases where you will have to pay the subcontractor a certain percentage of the job up front. Examples are kitchen cabinets, flooring, carpeting, and any other job where the subcontractor must pre-order custom styles and colors for you. But the risk here will still be minimal if you go with large, established companies.

You should always get at least two bids for each job, and here's why. Some subcontractors may "high ball" you, meaning that they will quote a very high price because they are very busy and do not want to deal with your job unless they get a huge profit. For example, I have a long asphalt driveway and my quotes varied significantly. My first quote from a busy subcontractor was for $18,400, and the second and third quotes from different companies were $11,500 and $12,200, respectively. All quotes were for the same ground preparation, the same base layer, the same asphalt thickness, the same square footage, and the same compaction. I went with the $12,200 bid because I felt more comfortable with that subcontractor. Had I not gotten more than one bid, I would have lost $6,200 ($18,400 - $12,200) and not even known it!

8.5 WORKING WITH SUBCONTRACTORS

There are several key things that you need to do that will provide an efficient, effective, and successful working relationship with your subcontractors. These items are communication, respect, inspection, and payment. Each of these is discussed below in more detail.

1) COMMUNICATION. Frequent and frank communications with your subcontractors is essential for success. In fact, poor communication is the leading cause of mistakes and errors being made in the home building process.

Subcontractors cannot read your mind, and you cannot read theirs. I found that the best way to minimize mistakes and reduce costly errors was to MEET WITH THE SUBCONTRACTOR'S FOREMAN WHEN THEY FIRST SHOW UP TO THE HOME SITE. Meet the foreman (or the boss of the on site workers), make sure he sees the plans, tell him what you expect, ask him if he has any questions, and give him your phone number so he can call if he needs you. Speaking with someone other than the foreman or boss may or may not be effective, so be careful here.

2) RESPECT. Always show respect for all of the workers at your home site. Leave them alone while they are working, stay out of their way, and let them do their job. No one likes to work with someone constantly standing over their shoulder and watching every move they make. Do not nit pick every little thing, but at the same time do not be afraid to speak up if you see something that is not correct or something being done improperly.

3) INSPECTION. You need to frequently inspect any work that the subcontractor does, usually on a daily basis, and report any problems or issues immediately to the subcontractor. If you are in doubt about something or if something just does not look right, go ahead and contact the subcontractor. The sooner you catch a mistake, the cheaper it is for you and the easier it is for the subcontractor to fix.

4) PAYMENT. Never pay the total amount of a subcontractor's bill until they are 100% finished. Repeat - DO NOT PAY IN FULL UNTIL THE SUBCONTRACTOR'S JOB IS TOTALLY COMPLETE. Withholding part of the payment until the work is complete is the only leverage you have for making sure the subcontractors show up when they are supposed to and complete their work when they are supposed to. The bottom line is that the subcontractor is there to make money, and if he/she has already been paid, then other jobs will take priority over yours. Use this final payment to your advantage!

Chapter 9

PHASE 1 CONSTRUCTION:
GROUNDWORK & FOUNDATION

At this point, you are now ready to start the actual construction of your new home. Using the system presented in this book, which is taking the complicated task of building a home and to breaking it up into small, manageable pieces, the job can be completed efficiently and effectively. This system continues in the next six chapters, where the actual construction process is broken down into six distinct phases of construction. These six phases will roughly coincide with your money draws and payments on your construction loan.

Each chapter will help to explain what will be happening during each phase, and is complemented with many photos and helpful hints for each activity. Phase 1 will cover the excavation, groundwork, and installing the foundation. Phase 2 will cover the framing and closing in the house to the point of keeping out the weather. Phase 3 covers the roughing-in of the mechanical, plumbing, and electrical systems. Phase 4 covers closing in the walls and adding interior trim. Phase 5 covers installation of the kitchen, bath, and other interior finish work. The final phase, Phase 6, covers all the finish work for the interior and the exterior. Let's start with Phase 1: Groundwork and Foundation.

9.1 DRIVEWAY, LOT CLEARING, AND EROSION CONTROL

DRIVEWAY. The first step is to provide an approved entrance to the property and building site. Most state or county transportation offices will require you to build the transition from the road to your driveway in a certain way, so you must check with the closest field office of your state highway department before you do anything near a state, city, or county-maintained road. If you do not follow these regulations, you may have to tear everything out, do it again according to the requirements, and possibly pay a fine.

For my driveway, I contacted the local field office of the Virginia Department of Transportation (VDOT) and asked if they had any requirements for driveways. They said there were definite requirements because my proposed driveway entrance was on a state-maintained road. The requirements were to: 1) use a culvert pipe of a certain diameter (12 inches) and length (30 feet), 2) use a certain type of gravel to form the base of the driveway near the road, and 3) use a larger type of gravel for a certain length of the driveway, near the road, to help minimize the amount of mud that may be brought onto the road. A typical driveway with culvert pipe installation is shown in Figure 9-1.

LOT CLEARING. This, of course, involves removing any trees, stumps, and brush that may interfere with the house's driveway, foundation and grading. If you do not have many trees and stumps to clear, and you are handy with a chain saw, then you may be able to save a little money by clearing out as much as you can yourself. But keep in mind that the excavator will have heavy equipment that will accomplish in minutes what it may take you hours or days to accomplish. Also, if you have any stumps, the excavator will need to remove these anyway. For my house, all that was involved for me was to cut a few acres of high grass, since my building site was basically in an open field.

Figure 9-1. A typical driveway installation showing the culvert pipe (for water flow), gravel, and erosion fence. Requirements for connecting your driveway to a state-maintained road will vary by state and region.

EROSION CONTROL. Many states and localities now have environmental laws and regulations that limit the amount of runoff and sediment that may make its way into streams and rivers from construction sites. These environmental measures help to protect our streams, rivers, and bays from becoming clogged with mud, sediment, and pollution. To help control this runoff of mud and sediment after moderate to heavy rains, your local officials may require you to install an erosion

85

fence on the downhill side or sides of your construction site. If your site is in a hilly area that is very close to a stream or river, even more stringent measures may need to be taken. An installed erosion fence is shown in Figure 9-1.

HELPFUL HINT: If your locality requires erosion control measures, you must have the erosion control measures in place, inspected, and approved before any construction starts. If you do not, you may receive a heavy fine!

If an erosion fence is required, you may be able to save some money by doing it yourself. But it is not as easy as just pounding a few stakes into the ground; you must dig a 4 to 6 inch trench to insert the base of the erosion fence. My excavation contractor wanted $900 to install about 300 feet of erosion fence, so I decided to just do it myself. I bought 300 feet of erosion fence at a local building supply store for about $90, then I went to a rental store and rented a power trencher for one day for about $160. It was hard work, but I finished the fence in less than a day, and I saved $650 by doing it myself.

9.2 EXCAVATION

Your excavation contractor will bring in some heavy equipment, such as bulldozers and front end loaders, to dig the area for your home's foundation. The amount of digging will of course depend upon whether you will be building on a basement, crawl space, or concrete slab. Before any digging is done, make sure you meet at the site with the excavation contractor. Bring your survey plat, foundation drawings, a 50- or 100-foot tape measure, and some wooden marking stakes. Be there with the excavation contractor to physically mark the ground where the foundation will go. All you need to do is to mark the corners, and the excavation contractor will take care of the rest.

The time to do the excavating will depend on how much your lot slopes, how much preparation work is required, and the type of foundation you will be using. My house involved digging out for a full basement, and took about 2 full days of work by the excavator.

HELPFUL HINT: Make sure the excavator digs to the proper depth to ensure that your finished house will sit on the lot as your drawings show. Don't be afraid to go over your drawings in detail and to ask questions to verify how the finished house will sit on the lot.

HELPFUL HINT: If you live in an area with many large buried rocks, your excavation cost may go up significantly because the rocks may be difficult to remove. Local excavators can tell you if rocks are a problem in your area.

9.3 FOOTERS AND FOUNDATION

Footers are the underground concrete pads that the foundation walls and any other support piers or posts will sit on. The footers must sit on stable, undisturbed ground (or sometimes called virgin soil) at a depth that is below the frost line in your area. The stable, undisturbed ground must be compact enough to support the house without any settling. The frost line is the depth of the ground that does not freeze during the winter months, and varies by region. If the ground is not stable, or if the footers sit above the frost line, then you can expect differential settling and frost heave to occur at your foundation. This would involve very expensive repairs that you do not want, so make sure all footers and foundation work are done by a reputable contractor who knows these codes. If your locality requires inspections, the inspector will not let any concrete footers be poured unless the soil is stable and at the correct depth. A typical concrete footer for a masonry foundation wall is shown in Figure 9-2.

HELPFUL HINT: After the footers are poured, carefully measure them to ensure that all dimensions are correct. Luckily, I measured mine, and one section of the concrete footer was off by 2 feet! The subcontractor immediately and easily corrected the problem. If this incorrect dimension was not found until after the concrete foundation walls were poured, the result would have been an expensive and time consuming mistake.

All houses require some type of foundation walls or supports that the house's wood framing will be sitting on. The most common types of foundations are basements, crawl spaces, and slabs. The type of foundation that you will be using depends on your house plans and what region of the country you live in. For

Figure 9-2. Typical concrete footers that will be supporting poured concrete foundation walls.

example, most houses in northern climates that have cold winters will have basements because the frost line is so deep that anything except a basement is impractical. On the other hand, houses in beach areas with sandy and unstable soil must use deeply driven piles to provide support for the house. In warm climates where the frost line is very shallow, concrete slabs can be used.

For my house in central Virginia, the climate is mild and the frost line of 18 inches. This means that most homes in this area generally use a basement or crawlspace type of foundation. I used a basement foundation. My concrete footers were placed well below the frost line, and poured reinforced concrete was used for the foundation walls. A typical poured concrete foundation is shown in Figure 9-3. At the depth of my footers, the soil was very stable. If the soil had not been stable, the excavator would have had to dig deeper and/or steel reinforcing bars (called re-bar) would have to be used at the unstable areas of the footers.

For whatever type of foundation you will have, especially for a basement or crawlspace, one of the most important things you must do for the long term is to KEEP WATER OUT AND AWAY FROM THE FOUNDATION. A key part of this is done before the foundation is backfilled with dirt, and involves spraying a special waterproof coating on the exterior foundation walls that will be below grade, and then installing a perimeter drainage system around the base of the foundation. This drainage system will collect and direct any water in the foundation area to a point safely down slope and away from the house. Any reputable concrete or foundation contractor will know what works best in your area for waterproofing.

HELPFUL HINT: The effectiveness of the perimeter drain depends on how neatly the gravel, drain hoses, and membrane were placed around the foundation. These drains hoses can easily become disconnected, crushed, or clogged with dirt or mud, so inspect this closely before the foundation is backfilled!

Figure 9-3. A typical foundation made with poured concrete foundation walls. In this photo, the basement concrete slab has also been poured.

HELPFUL HINT: The first line of defense against water intrusion in basements or foundations is not the underground perimeter drain, but a good roof gutter and downspout system. The downspouts must be extended to deposit water at least 8 to 10 feet away from and down slope from the foundation. Underground drain pipes for the downspouts work well for this, and can be easily installed by your landscape contractor. Chapter 14 covers this important item in more detail.

9.4 UNDERGROUND PLUMBING

After the foundation walls are up, the next step is for your plumber to install underground plumbing. This consists of running any drain piping and/or supply piping that will be under the foundation. The plumber will usually start at the location where the main drain line will exit the foundation, then plan the piping runs back from that point. To avoid future water intrusion problems and to allow the proper slope for drainage, it is usually a good idea to locate the drain line exit (and possibly the supply line piping) underneath the poured concrete footer. Typical underground plumbing installations are shown in Figures 9-4 and 9-5.

Figure 9-4. A typical installation of underground plumbing. After this plumbing passes an inspection, the entire floor area will be covered with 4 inches of gravel and 4 inches of concrete.

Figure 9-5. Typical underground plumbing. Note the area on the right where the main drain pipe exits the foundation under the concrete footer. The darker vertical pipe near this exit is a backflow valve that will prevent any sewage from backing up into the house.

As with any subcontractor, meet with the plumbing foreman on site, before any work starts, to go over the plan for running the pipes. A good and experienced plumber will be able to quickly point out any difficulties that may be encountered, and will discuss possible solutions and with you. It is also a good idea to show up regularly at the site to discuss any problems or issues with the plumbing foreman while the crew is still there and working.

HELPFUL HINT: Take photographs that show the locations of all the underground piping before it is covered up. This will serve as a handy reference in the future, and may help if any plumbing problems are discovered later.

9.5 SLABWORK

Concrete slabwork is otherwise known as pouring a concrete floor. It involves preparing the area and pouring a concrete slab for the basement floor (if your home has a basement) and garage floor. After the underground plumbing has been completed and inspected, the basement floor or garage floor is covered with approximately 4 inches of gravel and a layer of thick plastic sheeting (to keep moisture from seeping up through the concrete). Next a roll of steel reinforcing grid, and possibly some steel re-bar, is laid out over the plastic sheet for strength and to help prevent the concrete from cracking. Some areas may use a special type of concrete that has fiberglass particles mixed in, which eliminates the need for the steel reinforcing grid. That special concrete is used in my area and was used for my house. This saved considerable material and labor costs.

HELPUL HINT: In addition to the exterior perimeter drain around the foundation, it is also a good idea to now have your concrete subcontractor install an interior perimeter drainage system. This involves running collector pipes around the interior foundation walls and draining them into a sump pit. Any water collected in the sump pit is then pumped back to the outside and away from the foundation with a sump pump. This is just about a necessity if you have a basement foundation, and will serve as good, relatively cheap insurance against future water problems.

The standard depth of a typical concrete slab is 4 inches, but may even be deeper if a structural wall or support will rest directly above that area of the slab. This extra depth of concrete may also require steel re-bar, and is often referred to as a grade beam. This will be reflected in your foundation drawings, and make sure the subcontractor is aware of any grade beams.

Just before any concrete is poured, the prepared areas may need to be inspected by the local building inspector. If your area does not require an inspection for the slab, then make sure that you meet with the subcontractor just before the slab is poured so that you can inspect the prep work and to ask any questions before the concrete is poured.

HELPFUL HINT: As concrete cures, cracks and gaps will form due to slight shrinkage of the concrete. A general rule of thumb is that concrete will shrink approximately 1/8 inch for every 20 feet. This is why the subcontractor will put in separation lines every 20 feet or so to help guide the cracking that will occur. In general, slight cracks in concrete slabs are common and are not structurally significant. So do not worry about slight cracks that meet this rule of thumb, and do not blame the subcontractor for minor cracks. Instead, just ask the subcontractor to fill in any cracks with special filler concrete made for that purpose. If large, wide cracks more than 1/8 to 1/4 inch form, then the slab's base was probably not adequately repaired or the concrete mix was not correct. If this is the case, an knowledgeable engineer must be consulted immediately.

HELPFUL HINT: To help prevent cracking of the slab, try to keep the slab covered with plastic sheeting for up to 7 days to help retain moisture. The more moisture the concrete can retain while it is curing, the stronger the concrete will be.

9.6 ROUGH GRADE

After the exterior underground walls are waterproofed, the exterior perimeter drain system is installed, and the foundation is complete, the area around the foundation can be backfilled by the excavator. This is a simple process where the excavator will push the dirt back into the open area, compact it, and set a rough grade around the entire perimeter of the foundation to make sure that any water will flow away from the house.

HELPFUL HINT: Before the foundation is backfilled, remove any scraps of wood or other materials that may be covered. Removing the wood helps to prevent future termite problems, and removal of any other debris will help prevent future ground settling and will help to maintain the proper slope away from the foundation.

Since I used a poured concrete foundation, it was acceptable to backfill the foundation and to set the rough grade before any framing was in place. For other types of foundations, such as masonry unit (otherwise known as concrete block or brick) construction, backfilling at this point is not recommended until the wood framing for the floor above is installed. This is because the foundation walls may collapse from the weight and pressure of the backfill if the proper support framing is not in place. A good and experienced excavator will not backfill a foundation that is not ready to be backfilled because they do not want to be liable for any collapsed walls. So if you have any doubts or questions on this, just ask the excavator.

At this point the entire foundation system is complete, and the house is ready to begin framing. This is covered in the next chapter.

Chapter 10

PHASE 2 CONSTRUCTION: FRAMING & CLOSE-IN

This next phase of construction is where the house really starts to come together. The house will be framed, roofs put on, windows and doors installed, porches and decks constructed, and siding and trim installed. This phase is often called closing the house in, or in other words, protecting the inside from rain and weather. This closing in of the house starts with the framing.

10.1 FRAMING

The framing of a house refers to the assembling of wood or steel components that form the floors, walls, and roof of a house. Wood studs, joists, panels, decking, and trusses are typically used for framing. Figures 10-1 through 10-5 show typical houses at various stages of framing. There is so much involved with wood framing techniques and practices that it is beyond the scope of this book. But again, you do not need to be an expert in this area because you are hiring an experienced expert (your framing subcontractor) to do the job for you.

Figure 10-1. Framed walls in a basement area.

Your framing contractor will probably spend more time working on site than any other subcontractor. It is absolutely vital that the framing subcontractor that you hire be knowledgeable, reliable, and dependable. After all, when the framing starts, you need the framing subcontractor to get the framing up as quickly as possible and to get the house closed in and under roof before rain begins to take its toll. Kiln dried lumber and typical plywood or oriented strand board (OSB) panels are designed to survive several wet and dry cycles, but months of exposure to rain will eventually cause the wood to rot or warp and the plywood or OSB panels to delaminate. You do not want this to happen to your new house!

Figure 10-2. Typical framing for the floor just above the foundation.

In my area, the house building market was hot and all the framing contractors were very busy working for big builders. This left the framing subcontractors little or no time for framing houses for single house builders like me because there was no hope of repeat business. But I was lucky and landed one of the best framing subcontractors in the area. This company was owned by a man named Robert, and Robert was well known in the area and had a solid reputation for excellence and quality work. Robert and his crew were very reliable, showed up when he said they would, and did an absolutely outstanding job. Robert and his crew could just look at the drawings and easily project any possible problem areas or identify any drawing mistakes. When issues did come up during construction, Robert worked directly with the lumberyard or truss supplier to come up with a good solution to get the job done right.

Figure 10-3. Typical interior framing that shows walls, floors, and stairs.

Why am I telling you how great my framing subcontractor was? The answer is because YOU need a framing subcontractor like Robert, too, that will make your home building experience as efficient and relatively stress-free as possible. Here is how to find a framing subcontractor like Robert. First, ask anyone that you may know in the home building business this question - who is the best framing subcontractor in the area? If you do not know anyone in the home building business in your area, ask your salesperson at your building supply store (refer to section 8.3 of this book) who they would recommend, then pursue their recommendation. DO NOT GAMBLE by not getting a recommendation on this subcontractor, or it could be a disaster for you. Believe me when I tell you that any good lumberyard salesperson that has been around for a few years knows what framing contractors have a good reputation, and which ones do not.

Figure 10-4. First and second floor framing is complete, and is ready for the installation of roof trusses.

Once you have a recommended framing subcontractor, you must meet with them to go over your drawings, and if you feel comfortable with that subcontractor, get on their schedule at least 3 months before the projected start date of your framing. My framing was set to start on September 15, so I got on Robert's schedule in June. This was far enough ahead for him so that he could schedule his other jobs around mine, and to helped to ensure that my job would not be bumped off his busy schedule.

So the key points here are: 1) get knowledgeable recommendations for the best framer, and 2) get on the framer's schedule at least 3 months in advance. This worked for me, and will probably work for you, too.

Figure 10-5. Installation of roof trusses using a crane.

The photos in this section roughly correspond to the order of the framing that will take place. The process will take approximately 3 to 6 weeks, depending on the size and complexity of your house. In general, this is the order in which a typical framing job for a two level house with a basement will proceed:

1) Install sill plates at top of foundation walls.

2) Build basement support walls or set basement beams.

3) Build remaining basement walls.

4) Set floor joists and decking for first level floor.

5) Build first level exterior walls.

6) Build first level interior walls.

7) Set floor joists and decking for second level floor.

102

8) Build second level exterior walls.

9) Build second level interior walls.

10) Set roof trusses in place.

11) Install roof decking.

After the exterior framing is complete, the framing crew will need to come back a few more times to finish up interior details for stairs, supports, fire stops, drywall nailing surfaces, and possibly repair any areas damaged by mechanical, plumbing, or electrical subcontractors.

HELPFUL HINT: If you will be using large one-piece fiberglass bathtubs or showers, be aware that they are too large to fit through doors, and must be set in place before the framing for that area is complete.

HELPFUL HINT: Specify the use of special house wrap (typically called Tyvek) to keep out wind and air leaks to reduce future energy costs. This wrap will also protect any exposed wood from rain until the siding is installed. All exterior wood surfaces must be completely covered and carefully taped together for this wrap to be effective. This is well worth the extra cost, especially in colder climates.

HELPFUL HINT: There will be a whole lot of sawdust and scrap wood everywhere during the framing process. Try to clean up and sweep up as often as you can. The less mess that you have, the better, and your framer will appreciate it.

HELPFUL HINT: Consider giving your framing subcontractor signature authority for your account at your building supply store. I did, and it made life much easier for everyone. This will save you a lot of time because it allows the framer to go to the store, get the materials he needs immediately, and get right back to work. You can easily keep track of what your framer orders and picks up by observing the detailed monthly invoices that you will receive.

10.2 ROOFING

As soon as the framing crew gets finished with the roof decking (or sometimes called subroofing), get the roofing subcontractor in there as quickly as practical to get the roof covering installed. This must be done to protect the roof decking, which is usually rated plywood or OSB, from repeated wet/dry cycles caused by rain. As stated earlier, roof decking is made to withstand a few wet/dry cycles without delaminating, but not for weeks or months of rain. You can tell if your roof decking begins to delaminate, as it will appear wavy and you can easily pick apart the layers with a screwdriver. If it delaminates, it becomes structurally weakened, you will have to replace it!

The exact date that you need you roofing subcontractor to show up cannot be determined until your framer is finished. So the best thing to meet with the roofer two to three months before the projected install date, provide the appropriate roof drawings, pick out your materials and colors, and get an estimate. Give the roofer an approximate start date, but explain that it may change slightly, depending on the framer. The roofer will understand, and will put you on his schedule. As the roof start date nears, keep in contact with the roofer to keep you updated on his schedule.

A photo of my house, just after the roof was completed, is shown in Figure 10-6.

HELFUL HINT: If you are using the common asphalt/fiberglass roof shingles, go with the highest rated lifetime shingle that you can afford. 30-, 40-, and 50-year shingles are much thicker and will withstand winds much better than shingles with a lower yearly rating. Plus you may never have to replace the roof in your lifetime.

HELPFUL HINT: Tell the roofer to use thick waterproof membranes at all edges, valleys, adjoining walls, or any other irregular spot on your roof. This will greatly help to protect against any expensive water leakage into the house by ice dams or wind driven rain.

Figure 10-6. Framing, windows, doors (except garage doors), and roof are installed. Notice the installation of the white house wrap on all walls. The house is now considered "closed in", allowing work to start on the interior.

HELPFUL HINT: Insist that the roofer use high quality and long lasting "boots" over any plumbing vents that come through the roof. The cheap rubber boots that are most common will disintegrate after about 8 to 10 years and require expensive replacement. I specified high quality lead boots and flashing for my roof vents. Why get 50-year shingles if the cheap vent boots will only last 10 years?

10.3 WINDOWS AND EXTERIOR DOORS

After the roofing material is on, the final step for closing in the house from the weather is to install your windows and doors. This will be done by your framing subcontractor, and will probably only take a few days to complete, but will of course depend on the number of windows and doors and their complexity.

The typical lead time for doors and windows is typically 3 to 4 weeks, so it may be best to order them 5 to 6 weeks in advance of when you will need them. This will allow time for possible manufacturing errors or missed delivery dates so that your home building schedule is not affected. But the downside to this is that you do not want thousands of dollars worth of windows sitting around on the job site. The longer they are there, the more prone they are to damage or theft. The ideal solution would be to keep them at the lumberyard, but keep in mind that the lumberyard may not hold them for as long as you would like. Again, this is yet another area where your building material salesperson can help you out.

HELPFUL HINT: Buy only high quality windows and doors. The initial extra cost will more than pay for itself in a few years through increased energy savings and less repair or replacement expense.

HELPFUL HINT: If you are using wood framed windows, buy windows that have already been primed and painted at the factory. The slight extra cost will save you many hours of costly labor for your painter.

HELPFUL HINT: Have your windows and doors delivered to the inside of your garage. This will keep them out of the weather and relatively safe until the framers can install them.

10.4 DECKS, PORCHES, PATIOS, AND SIDEWALKS

Now is the time to build any porches, decks, or patios that have been planned. Your framing contractor will do the rough framing for porches, but may not want to deal with building the deck. A separate deck contractor may be a good idea anyway because that is the part of construction in which they specialize.

Concrete patios and sidewalks will require your concrete subcontractor again, and installation is a fairly straightforward process. The only decisions that you will need to make concern the length, width, and curvature of the patio and sidewalks, and possibly steps.

10.5 SIDING AND TRIM

Installation of the siding and trim is the last step in completely weatherproofing the exterior of your home. The siding material can be wood (painted or stained), vinyl, aluminum, stucco, brick, stone veneer, or other. The trim is usually aluminum or vinyl, and is used to cover the eaves and overhangs (otherwise known as soffitt and fascia), plus any other exposed areas that the siding will not cover. It may be best to go with the materials that are prevalent in your area, as different materials may work better in different climates.

For my house, I used brick on the front and right side, and up to the first floor level at the left side and rear. For the upper sections at the left side and rear, I used high quality beaded vinyl siding. For the trim, all fascia boards were covered (sometimes call capped) with aluminum, and vinyl panels were used for the soffitt and for the ceiling sections of my front and rear porches. This provided me with a house that was almost maintenance-free on the exterior (no painting!), which is exactly what I wanted. Figures 10-7 through 10-9 show various aspects of the siding and trim that are discussed in this section.

Figure 10-7. Left side of house showing brick siding, vinyl siding, aluminum capped fascia, vinyl soffitt panels, and aluminum gutters and downspouts.

HELPFUL HINT: If you will be using vinyl siding, purchase the highest quality vinyl that you can afford. More expensive vinyl siding is thicker and is less prone to warping or appearing wavy. Cheap vinyl siding will quickly become wavy and unsightly after just a few years.

Figure 10-8. Underside of front porch showing vinyl soffitt panels and aluminum capped fascia boards.

I used two subcontractors for the siding, one for the brick and one for the vinyl siding, trim, and gutters. My brick subcontractor was the only subcontractor that I had any kind of trouble with. He routinely did not show up when promised, would show up and work for several days, then would not be seen or heard from for many weeks at a time. I estimate that the construction of my house was delayed by a total of about two months because this. I could not bring in my vinyl siding contractor until the brick was complete, and it was somewhat aggravating to keep my house uncovered with siding and exposed to the elements for many months. He had obviously overbooked his schedule, and preferred to work for big builders who would provide him with repeat business. But I can say that he did an excellent job on my brickwork, as it was well done and looks beautiful.

As soon as the brick was completed, my vinyl siding subcontractor came in and put up all the siding, exterior trim, and installed gutters and downspouts in about two days! The crew had about 12 people who worked very quickly and efficiently. After the brick fiasco, it sure was nice to have a reliable subcontractor to come in and quickly complete his work. I had several good recommendations for the vinyl siding contractor, and it worked out well.

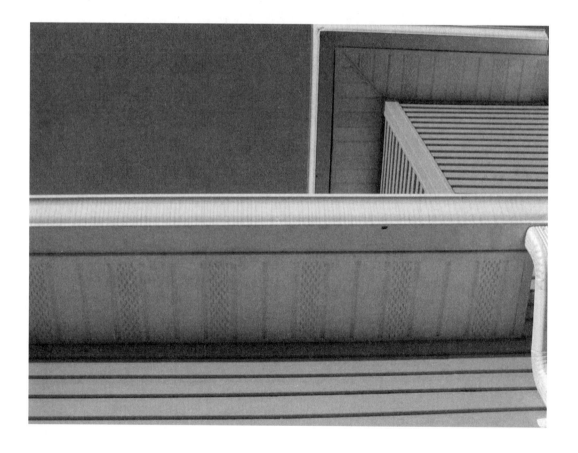

Figure 10-9. Looking up from the ground shows the vented soffitt panels that will help ventilate the roof and attic areas.

HELPFUL HINT: Use vented soffitt panels if possible. This will help to ventilate the roof area to keep it cooler in the summer and will help to prevent ice dams from forming in the winter.

HELPFUL HINT: Use the same subcontractor for siding, trim, and gutters and downspouts if possible. It will save time and money for you.

HELPFUL HINT: Buy long sections of 4 inch plastic drain hose and temporarily attach them to the end of each downspout to deposit water at least 12 feet from the foundation. This will keep water away from the foundation and prevent erosion under the downspout. This drain hose will be buried later by the landscape subcontractor.

At this point in the construction, the exterior of the house is complete and sealed from the weather. Now the interior work can begin. This interior work starts with the rough-in of the mechanical, plumbing, and electrical systems, and is covered in the next chapter.

Chapter 11

PHASE 3 CONSTRUCTION: ROUGH-IN SYSTEMS

Now that the interior is protected from the weather, the next phase of construction can begin. Phase 3 of the construction process focuses on the "rough-in" of the mechanical, plumbing, and electrical systems. "Rough-in" is the term commonly used for installing and running the ductwork, pipes, and wires throughout the interior of the house. This occurs just after the interior of the house is protected from rain and weather and before any interior walls are covered with insulation or drywall.

11.1 ROUGH-IN MECHANICAL SYSTEMS

The first rough-in system to be installed is the mechanical system, also known as the HVAC (heating, ventilation, and air conditioning) system. This is usually the first system to go in because the ductwork, furnace, and/or air handling units are relatively large and the places they can be located may be more limited that the plumbing and electrical system. In general, it is much easier for a plumbing pipe or electrical wire to go around a large duct, rather than vice versa.

There are many types of HVAC systems that can be used, and will usually be dictated by the type of climate at your house location. For example, colder climates may use pressurized hot water for heating, with no air conditioning. Moderate climates may use a gas or oil burning furnace, along with a central air conditioning unit, or maybe just a heat pump. Warmer climates may use a heat pump with central air conditioning, and/or require no central heat at all.

Since there are so many types and combinations of heating and cooling systems available, perhaps the best way for you to decide what to get is to take the advice of your HVAC subcontractor. A good HVAC subcontractor will examine your drawings, discuss various options with you, and propose the best solution for your needs and budget.

For my house in Virginia, I decided to go with a split system. For the large basement and first floor area, a high efficiency, forced air, natural gas furnace and central air conditioning unit was installed at a central location in the basement. This unit is shown in figure 11-1. This location was chosen because the ductwork for these areas could be relatively easily located between the floor joists for the first floor, and the ductwork would not take up any extra closet or floor space. This means that the air vents (also called registers) for the basement level would be located in the ceiling, and the registers for the first level would be located on the floor. For the second level, a high efficiency, forced air heat pump (supplying both heat and air conditioning) was installed in the attic area. Thus, the registers for the second level were located in the ceiling.

Since these were forced air systems, each system had its own air supply ductwork and its own return air ductwork. This split system was used to maximize heating and cooling efficiencies and for the ease of running the supply and return ductwork in a simple and efficient manner.

Figure 11-1. This photo shows a typical forced air, high efficiency gas furnace with a central air conditioning unit. The duct on the left is the main air return duct; it feeds into the bottom section of the furnace unit. This bottom section of the furnace unit contains the fan that is used to circulate air throughout the house. The center part of the furnace contains the gas burners, and the two large pipes coming from the top of the burner unit are the fresh air intake and exhaust pipes that travel to the exterior of the house. The section behind the two pipes is the central air conditioning unit.

HELPFUL HINT: Unless you plan on staying only a year or two in your new home, go with high efficiency furnaces, heat pumps, and air conditioning units. The extra up front cost will more than pay for itself within a few years through increased energy savings.

HELPFUL HINT: Use an HVAC subcontractor who will provide you with a computerized analysis report for the heating and cooling needs for your home. This analysis considers your floor plan, the amount of insulation, how many windows and doors, the direction that your house faces, and other factors to properly size the heating and cooling loads for your home. The analysis report will also recommend supply and return air duct sizes and locations to optimize the comfort and evenness of heating and cooling air.

HELPFUL HINT: If your locality requires an inspection of the HVAC system, then the analysis report must be done and a copy must be readily available to the inspector at the time of the inspection.

HELPFUL HINT: Meet your HVAC subcontractor on-site before any work starts to determine placements of furnaces and ductwork. The ductwork may have to take up closet or wall space that you may not realize. If this happens, ask the HVAC subcontractor to give you some different options.

HELPFUL HINT: If possible, bring in your plumbing subcontractor while your HVAC subcontractor is still working. Introduce them and ask if there are any potential problem areas or competition for space to run their ducts or pipes. There probably will be! This communication between these two subcontractors may save you from significant time, trouble, and cost over the next few weeks of construction.

HELPFUL HINT: Make sure that the HVAC installers do not cut into any structural beams or joists that may significantly weaken the structure. For example, support beams and floor joists cannot be completely or significantly cut out to run ductwork. But there are some acceptable standards for limited amounts of holes through the center of joists, and these standards must be strictly followed. Thoroughly inspect the ductwork installation, and refer to the joist manufacturer's instructions if you have any questions.

11.2 ROUGH-IN PLUMBING

The rough-in plumbing work can usually start after the HVAC ductwork and/or piping has been installed. This work involves the installation of drain/waste/vent (DWV) lines from each toilet, sink, bathtub, shower, and washing machine, and the installation of the hot water heater and cold and hot water supply lines to the fixtures as needed. Also included are installation of the hot water heater and any natural gas or propane lines.

HELPFUL HINT: If you will be using natural gas from a local gas company, contact your gas company early in the construction process to arrange an installation date for your gas service. In my area, the wait list for new gas service was 5 months!

The most common material used for the DWV lines is white PVC piping. Larger diameter PVC piping is used for main drain lines and toilets, while smaller diameter PVC piping is used for sink drains and vent pipes. Figure 11-2 shows a typical installation of some PVC piping running through a wall. The installation of the DWV system must be done by a licensed plumber, as there are numerous plumbing codes that specify strict piping size, slope, location, coupling, venting, and connection type requirements.

Figure 11-2. Typical wall in a bathroom showing the toilet flange (on the floor), the PVC drain and vent pipes, and copper supply pipes.

The most common materials for water supply piping are copper piping and polybutylene (PB) tubing. Copper piping uses rigid pipe and solder connections, while PB tubing uses flexible tubing with clamp connections. Figure 11-2 shows some typical copper supply piping. Copper piping is generally considered more durable and long lasting, but advances in plastics technology and PB tubing connectors and clamping tools have come a long way in recent years. If you are undecided on what type of supply line material to use, it would be wise to do some research on the internet and to discuss options with your plumbing subcontractor. As with the DWV piping, there are strict plumbing codes that must be followed for the installation of water supply lines, so a knowledgeable and licensed plumbing subcontractor is a must.

As mentioned previously, it would be wise to have the plumbing subcontractor start while the HVAC subcontractor is still working on site, or at least have the plumber meet with the HVAC subcontractor to discuss any issues. They will both be very grateful because they both know how much time and hassle it may save for them!

HELPFUL HINT: If low water pressure may be a problem in your area, tell the plumbing subcontractor to increase the pipe diameter to each bathroom or kitchen area. For example, instead of running a one-half inch diameter copper pipe to supply each bathroom area (shower, sink, and toilet), use a three-quarter inch diameter pipe to supply the water for that bathroom area. The extra cost is minimal and well worth it.

HELPFUL HINT: If low water pressure may be a problem in your area, tell the plumbing subcontractor to increase the underground pipe diameter from the municipal supply or well into your house. This will significantly increase your water pressure and flow rate.

HELPFUL HINT: Make sure that the plumbers do not cut into any structural beams or joists that may significantly weaken the structure. This is the same advice for the HVAC installation listed in section 11.1.

HELPFUL HINT: Meet with the plumber on-site before any work starts so that the plumber can show you exactly where the DWV and supply pipes will be installed. This is your chance to change pipe routings, if necessary.

HELPFUL HINT: If you want to install a central vacuum system, now is the time to install the piping for it. I installed a central vacuum system in my house, and we absolutely love the ease and convenience of this system.

11.3 ROUGH-IN ELECTRICAL

The rough-in electrical work starts immediately after the HVAC and plumbing are completed. This process involves installing the main breaker panel, installing a box for every receptacle, light, and appliance, and then running electrical wire between them. No wire connections are made during this rough-in phase, and the wires are left hanging out of each box.

The main breaker panel is usually located on a wall that is very close to the box that will hold the outside electric meter. Figure 11-3 shows a typical main breaker panel installation. In most areas, your electrician is responsible for all wiring past the electric meter, and your electric company is responsible for the supply wiring up to and including the meter.

HELPFUL HINT: Contact your electric company early in the construction process to arrange an installation date for your electrical service. In my area, the wait list for new electrical service is 3 to 4 months!

Any new construction follows a very strict electrical building code that specifies wire types, wire sizes, breaker types, breaker sizes, junction box sizes, receptacle box sizes, receptacle locations, ground fault circuit interrupter (GFCI) locations, and many other complex items. Unless you are a licensed and experienced electrician, don't even think about doing this work yourself. Running your house wiring may seem like a simple job, but it's not. There is a lot more wire to run than you would think there is, there is a lot more to know about wiring and circuits than you think there is. One wrong wire or one wire in the wrong place can later cause a fire or safety hazard.

Figure 11-3. This photo show two main breaker panels with wires coming from the top of each box to feed the house circuits, lights, and receptacles.

At your first meeting, you will need to provide your electrician with a floor plan drawing showing where your major appliances will be located and where every overhead light, switch, and receptacle will be located. Again, meet with the electrical subcontractor on-site before any work starts so that you can go over every detail where every electrical item will be located. If you are unsure about anything, just ask the electrician for options. Any experienced electrician can quickly spot any problem areas on your drawings and make good recommendations on how to fix them. Again, the electrical subcontractor is your hired expert, so use their expertise as much as possible.

HELPFUL HINT: For any long wire runs and for lights and/or for receptacles farthest from the breaker box, ask the electrician to increase the wire size for these circuits to prevent any flickering lights or brown outs.

HELPFUL HINT: For security purposes, install extra switches for all outside lights near a window in your bedroom. If you hear strange noises or something outside during the night, the ability to turn your outside lights on and off from your bedroom can provide extra security and peace of mind for you and your family.

If your locality requires inspections, now is the time for your inspector to come in and examine each of these systems. These inspections must be done before any insulation is added and before any of the walls are closed in with drywall or wallboard. Pay close attention if the inspector finds anything that does not meet the local building code because any problems identified and fixed now will save you a lot of time, money, and aggravation later!

This completes the rough-in phase for the mechanical, plumbing, and electrical systems. If you are unsure or uncomfortable with your knowledge of these systems, be aware that there are many books out there on these subjects that cover everything for novices up through experts. You are encouraged to research any area that you are not comfortable with, and to ask your subcontractor for advice, recommendations, and/or further explanation.

11.4 INSULATION

After all the ductwork, pipes, and wires have been installed and inspected, the walls are ready for insulation. Note that in most cases, the most important insulation, the ceiling insulation, cannot be installed yet. This is because you must wait until the drywall for the ceiling is in place. The ceiling insulation is by far the most critical for keeping your house comfortable, so this is one place where you absolutely do not want to skimp. Go with the next highest R-value above what is recommended for your area. For example, if the minimum for your area is R-30, go with R-38 in the attic.

Of all the work that needs to be done on your house, installing insulation is one of the few things that can be done by yourself, and without hiring and paying an insulation contractor. After all, installing insulation on the walls involves simply buying the insulation batts or rolls, cutting them to length, and then stapling them to the wood framing or rolling them out in the attic. But wait! I had planned on doing this work myself and saving some money, but I had an insulation subcontractor do it instead. Why? Because after I priced out how much insulation I would need, I got an estimate from a reputable insulation subcontractor using the same materials, and his bid for material and labor was within $50 of what I would have paid for material alone! Apparently, his discount for buying insulation in bulk offset his labor cost for installation. This was fine with me because it saved me 3 or 4 days of work.

Caulking and sealing gaps will help to prevent drafts and is also an important part of the insulating process. This includes sealing gaps around windows, doors, vent openings, ceiling fixtures, framing gaps, and any other area where outside air may be able to leak in or conditioned inside air may be able to leak out.

HELPFUL HINT: Use the maximum R-value available that will fit in your wall cavities. The increased comfort and energy savings will more than offset the extra initial cost.

HELPFUL HINT: If you are going to do the wall insulation yourself, make sure you are well aware of the hows and whys of insulation types, R-values, vapor barriers, caulking and sealing, and proper installation techniques.

HELPFUL HINT: If a subcontractor installs your insulation, inspect every wall carefully to make sure there are no open areas and that any gaps are caulked or sealed, especially around electrical boxes.

HELPFUL HINT: Make sure that any bathtubs or showers that are next to an outside wall are heavily insulated between the wall and the tub or shower. This area is frequently overlooked and results in very cold tubs and showers.

HELPFUL HINT: Buy some extra insulation to use for soundproofing between certain rooms and to wrap around any plumbing pipes in any room where you wish to minimize any water pipe or drain noise.

After the insulation is inspected, you are ready to close in the walls. This phase of construction is covered in the next chapter.

Chapter 12

PHASE 4 CONSTRUCTION: INTERIOR WORK

Phase 4 of construction is where the interior of your home really begins to take shape. This phase involves enclosing each room's ceilings and walls with drywall (or other materials), finishing the drywall seams, installing interior trim (such as floor molding, chair rail, and crown molding), doing any ceramic tile work (such as bathroom or shower tile), completing the first stage of the painting process, and completing the final drywall touch up (sometimes called point up).

12.1 DRYWALL

Most residential construction today uses drywall (also called gypsum board or wallboard) as the material of choice for covering interior wall surfaces. This material is strong, durable, relatively easy to install, and easy to repair. Others may choose to use plaster walls, but this wall covering is becoming rare because it requires skilled craftsman to apply the plaster and requires much more time, labor and cost than drywall. I used drywall in my house, and you probably will, too.

The steps involved with drywall installation are:

    1) hanging the drywall

    2) taping the drywall joints

    3) applying joint compound to drywall joints and fasteners

    4) sanding the joint compound

    4) point up of drywall after the primer coat of paint

Drywall sheets usually come in 4 ft x 8 ft or 4 ft x 12 ft sizes. Professional drywall subcontractors use the larger sheets because there are less joints or seams that need to be taped and finished. Even though the larger sheets are heavier and harder to handle, experienced drywall subcontractors have the people, equipment, and expertise to handle the job.

If you are considering doing the drywall work yourself instead of hiring a subcontractor, you may want to reconsider. Hanging hundreds of sheets of drywall is very hard work, and you must be very strong and have one or two very strong helpers. Then you must tape and finish hundreds or thousands of feet of drywall seams and thousands of nail or screw heads. Finishing drywall seams properly and efficiently requires an experienced person with specialized skill. A novice could do it, but it will probably take them weeks or months to do it right and to get it right.

HELPFUL HINT: For hanging drywall, use the "glue and screw" method. This involves applying construction adhesive to the wood framing, then using screws to secure the drywall to the framing. This results in stronger, stiffer walls and may require fewer screws to install and finish.

HELPFUL HINT: Use green drywall board in bathroom areas. This type of drywall is colored green and is more moisture resistant than standard drywall boards (but not moisture proof). This will help the walls to withstand the moisture and steam coming from showers and bathtubs.

For my house, I used a drywall subcontractor, and had him take care of everything including ordering the drywall, having it delivered and unloaded, hanging, and finishing. His crew worked quickly and efficiently and did a good job. Doing it this way saved me weeks of back-breaking lifting and tedious taping and finishing. This was another instance where a turn-key subcontractor worked out well and saved me time and aggravation.

12.2 INTERIOR TRIM CARPENTRY

After the drywall is installed and finished, it is time to install the interior trim. This is called interior trim carpentry or finish carpentry, and involves installing all interior doors, door trim, window sills and trim, baseboard trim, chair rail, crown molding, stair trim, and possibly closet shelving or other specialized shelving.

Experienced trim subcontractors are highly skilled craftsmen who can quickly and precisely cut trim pieces to fit perfectly with little or no gaps. If you have ever attempted to use a miter saw and a coping saw to get two pieces of crown molding to fit together nicely in a corner, you can quickly appreciate how much skill is required for finish carpentry.

For my house, I supplied all the materials and my trim carpenter supplied the labor. Most trim carpenters prefer to work this way to lessen their risk. For the materials, I simply measured the linear footage in each room for each trim type, added it all up, and called in the order to my building material supplier. The material was delivered the next day. But I had to order my interior doors well before I needed them, as they required a three week lead time from the manufacturer.

I also had a rather complicated stair railing system that my trim carpenter installed. My building supplier had me pick out the style of railing, then he came out and measured to determine exactly what material I needed. If you have a complicated stair railing system, an experienced trim carpenter is a must-have. It is just too difficult a job for a novice to attempt.

HELPFUL HINT: If you plan on having stained trim instead of painted trim, then the trim work process becomes much harder because the moldings must fit much more precisely, and the moldings will probably not be installed until after all the wall painting is finished. For these reasons, you can expect to pay your trim carpenter and painter much more if you use stained trim.

12.3 PAINTING- STAGE 1

Now that the wallboard is up and finished and the wood trim is installed, the first stage of painting can begin. This first stage involves the application of a primer coat of paint to all exposed surfaces. This primer coat is absolutely necessary to properly seal the drywall and wood and to help the following layers of paint to be even and uniform.

The easiest and most cost effective way to apply the primer is by spraying. This is why the primer coat is applied before and flooring, kitchen cabinetry, bathroom vanities, or finish trim for plumbing, HVAC, or electrical systems is installed. Paint spray will be everywhere, and all windows and other areas will be masked off where overspray is not acceptable. A good paint subcontractor has the specialized tools, spray equipment, masking material, and expertise to get this job done quickly and thoroughly.

Of course, no other subcontractor can be working in the house while the inside is being sprayed.

HELPFUL HINT: Make sure your painting subcontractor uses high quality primer. Cheap primer formulations may not adhere as well, and may cost you more later through frequent repaintings. You must have a good base coat or primer!

HELPFUL HINT: Make sure your painter does a light sanding of the walls after the primer coat is dry. This is an important step for having smooth, good-looking walls.

HELPFUL HINT: If the interior is to be all one color or if you have many rooms that will be the same color, some painters may prefer to also spray on the first finish coat at this time. Spraying may save you money and time. Be sure to thoroughly discuss this option with your painting subcontractor.

12.4 DRYWALL POINT UP

After the primer coat of paint is applied and lightly sanded, any significant imperfections in the drywall joints or nail/screw areas will be magnified and made more visible. This is when your drywall subcontractor will come back in to repair or "point up" any of these areas. The process involves applying more joint compound to form a smooth surface at each identified area, letting it dry, then sanding it smooth.

Many drywall subcontractors use a simple incandescent utility light to help highlight any areas that need more work. Holding the light directly next to a wall or ceiling area will create shadows in any area where the drywall joint is not smooth. After the point up is done, the drywall subcontractor's job is done.

HELPFUL HINT: Use your own utility light to check the walls and ceiling while the drywall subcontractor is still on site. If you find any areas that were missed, let them know immediately so the area can be repaired before the subcontractor leaves.

12.5 BATHROOM TILE

If you plan on having ceramic tile around your bathtubs or showers, or anywhere else in your bathrooms or home, now is the time for the tile installation. The primer coat of paint is on the walls, and you will not have to worry about any over-spray on the tiles. Note that most tiles must be installed over cement board, and not drywall or moisture resistant drywall. If drywall gets wet, it crumbles, but cement board will not crumble or weaken when wet.

A good, experienced tile contractor knows what works and what does not work in the long term. This is especially true for ceramic tile in shower floor areas. If the floor and base area is not properly prepared, it will leak! These areas are notorious for being okay for a while, then gradually leaking over time, causing much frustration, grief, and expensive rip out, repair, and replacement costs. These leaks usually result from a small hole in the floor's rubber membrane, insufficient slope toward the drain on the floor, or poor preparation of the base area.

HELPFUL HINT: If you will have a tile floor in your shower, it would be very wise to research the proper installation techniques, tell your subcontractor that you are very concerned about future leaks, and to make sure the subcontractor uses the correct materials, the proper installation techniques, and is very careful in this area. Do not become a leaking tile floor victim!

12.6 PAINTING - STAGE 2

The second stage of the painting process (stage 1 was the application of primer) can now be accomplished, and involves extensive caulking of gaps and the application of the first coat of paint. Most painters prefer to apply this first coat now because it is easier to apply paint to the walls, doors, and moldings without all of the cabinets, vanities, and HVAC/plumbing/electrical trim in place. This is a big job that requires a lot of preparation work to do it right, but an experienced painting crew can probably accomplish this in a week or less. Of course, the actual time required depends on the size of your house and the complexity of your walls, ceilings, and moldings.

HELPFUL HINT: Use only high quality paints and caulks. Using the cheaper paints will not look as good, and will make you have to re-paint in a few years. With paint or caulk, you get what you pay for.

HELPFUL HINT: Be aware that if you would like a variety of different paint colors for different rooms, your painter will have to spend much more time on your job and it will cost you much more. If you want to save some money, try to stick with many of the same neutral colors in many of your rooms.

After this stage of painting is complete, other interior work can now begin. This is covered in the next chapter.

Chapter 13

PHASE 5 CONSTRUCTION:
INTERIOR FINISH WORK

Now that the walls are in and have a base coat of paint, the major interior finish items can be installed. This phase 5 of construction involves the installation of major interior items including the flooring (hardwood, vinyl, and tile), the kitchen (cabinets and countertops), bathroom cabinets and vanities, and finish work for the mechanical (thermostats, registers, etc.), plumbing (sinks, toilets, faucets, etc.), and electrical (switches, receptacles, fixtures, etc.) systems.

13.1 FLOORING

Flooring needs to be in place before any cabinets, vanities, toilets, etc. are installed. The most common types of flooring used are hardwood flooring, vinyl sheets or squares, and ceramic or composite tile. There are many options available on types, grades, quality, colors, and cost for each flooring type, so it is in your best interest to visit a full service flooring showroom to see what range of flooring is available.

133

Going with one flooring store or subcontractor for all of your flooring will definitely save you time and money. A subcontractor that has a large selection, competitive pricing, and offers installation services will reduce the number of people you will have to negotiate with, coordinate schedules with, and get billed from. Plus you may get a discount for purchasing and installing all of your flooring as a package.

HELPFUL HINT: This is one subcontractor that you will probably have to pay up front for materials. But the risk is small if you choose a larger subcontractor or store that is firmly established in your area.

13.2 KITCHEN CABINETS AND COUNTERTOPS

After the flooring is laid in your kitchen, the cabinets and countertops can now be installed. This is another area where there is a wide range of types, styles, quality, and cost for both cabinets and countertops. Your best bet here is to go with a full service company or subcontractor that can help to assess your specific needs, discuss your options, provide free kitchen design and drawings, provide many styles and options for cabinetry and countertops, and offers professional installation services.

HELPFUL HINT: Due to the very wide price range for cabinets and countertops, always ask for a complete package price for materials, delivery, and installation. Different materials may cost more or less to deliver and install.

HELPFUL HINT: This is another subcontractor where you may have to pay some money up front. Again, going with a larger established store or subcontractor will greatly reduce your risk.

13.3 BATHROOM VANITIES

After the flooring is installed in your bathrooms, the vanities can be installed. Vanities are simply the cabinets in your bathroom with a countertop and sink installed. As with the kitchen, there are many types, styles, and cost ranges here. Use your prospective subcontractor to help explain all of your options and help you to decide what is best for you and your budget.

HELPFUL HINT: Use your kitchen subcontractor to also supply and install your bathroom vanities. Again, this will lessen the number of subcontractors that you must deal with and make things much easier for you.

13.4 FINISH MECHANICAL

Now that your flooring and cabinetry is installed, your mechanical or HVAC subcontractor can now come back in to install any air registers, return air grilles, radiator trim, thermostats, and to test and balance your system. This will complete your HVAC subcontractor's work, so make sure that everything is in place and you are satisfied with the system before you make final payment. Figure 13-1 shows a checklist that can help you do this.

HELPFUL HINT: Have the HVAC subcontractor show you the locations of the furnace, cooling system, all ductwork, and thermostats, and to demonstrate the operation of each. That way, if anything is wrong, the subcontractor will see it and will fix it, plus you get to ask any questions that you may have.

HELPFUL HINT: Do not run air conditioning units if the outside temperature is below about 60 degrees F. If you do, you risk damage to your system. Ask the HVAC subcontractor about your specific cooling equipment.

FIGURE 13-1. HVAC CHECKLIST

- ❏ Heating and cooling equipment installation is complete
- ❏ Furnace unit works and puts out adequate heat
- ❏ Cooling unit works and puts out cold air
- ❏ Condensate drains installed on cooling unit
- ❏ Condensate drains properly
- ❏ Ductwork or piping is adequately sealed
- ❏ Air filters installed (for forced air systems)
- ❏ Air register or radiator placements and adequacy
- ❏ Adequate combustion air available for furnace
- ❏ Gas/oil service line does not leak
- ❏ Gas/oil service line adequately supported
- ❏ Furnace vents properly (no carbon monoxide present)
- ❏ Thermostat works properly

13.5 FINISH PLUMBING

The finish plumbing work involves the installation and final connection of all sinks, sink faucets, sink drains, toilets, dishwasher, bathtub faucets and drains, shower faucets and drains, all associated trim pieces, and anything else with a water supply or drain. Once everything is installed, it is imperative that you thoroughly inspect the entire plumbing system before you make your final payment to the plumbing subcontractor. Figure 13-2 shows a checklist to help you do this.

HELPFUL HINT: Have the plumber take you around to show you the locations of all piping and valves, and to demonstrate the operation of each valve and faucet.

That way, if anything is wrong, the plumber will see it and will fix it, plus you will get to ask any questions that you may have.

HELPFUL HINT: If a sink or tub drain makes a gurgling sound while draining, then chances are that the drain venting is incorrect, blocked, or incorrectly installed.

HELPFUL HINT: Make sure you run the dishwasher and check under it and in the sink drain area for any supply leaks, drain leaks, or venting problems. Initial dishwasher installations are notorious for leaks.

FIGURE 13-2. PLUMBING CHECKLIST

❑ Correct faucets installed

❑ Adequate pressure and flow rate at every faucet

❑ Shut off valves installed at every fixture

❑ Hot and cold water lines correctly installed at each sink, tub, shower

❑ No leaks in any supply piping or drain piping

❑ Drainage rate at each fixture is adequate

❑ Drain traps installed at every sink, tub, shower

❑ No gurgling sounds at any drain

❑ Drains vent at the exterior roof

❑ Refrigerator ice maker water line installed and does not leak

❑ No pounding noises when water is abruptly turned on or off

❑ Main water shut off valve is readily accessible and works

❑ Toilets flush and fill adequately and do not leak

❑ Hot water tank is adequately sized

❑ Hot water tank works

❑ Hot water tank thermostat is set correctly

13.6 FINISH ELECTRICAL

Finish electrical work involves the installation of all breakers in the electrical panel, all switches, receptacles, ground fault circuit interrupters (GFCI) in the kitchen, bathrooms, and exterior, all overhead lighting, all appliance hookups (furnace, heat pump, dishwasher, etc.), and all associated cover plates and trim. Note that if you plan on having anything except very basic light fixtures, then the electrical subcontractor will probably require you to purchase these fixtures separately. Be careful with your budget here because the light fixtures in your house add up quickly, and certain styles can be very expensive. The actual installation of the fixtures that you buy should be included in the electrical subcontractor's bid. Make sure this is clear before the start of the electrical work.

As with the HVAC and plumbing, it is imperative that you thoroughly inspect and test the entire electrical system before you make your final payment to the electrical subcontractor. Figure 13-3 shows a checklist to help you do this.

HELPFUL HINT: Purchase a simple 3-prong electrical circuit tester for about $10 at any large building supply store. Use it to check for power and correct wiring at all receptacles. It will have 3 lights that will indicate if the receptacle is working and if the hot, neutral, and ground wires are correct. Make sure you get one that has a push button tester to check your GFCI receptacles.

HELPFUL HINT: If your area requires inspections, then make sure that the main panel cover is off when the electrical inspector gets there. In my area, if the panel cover is on, the inspectors are instructed to fail the inspection because of time and safety reasons!

FIGURE 13-3. ELECTRICAL CHECKLIST

- ❑ Main panel box installed correctly
- ❑ No loose wires or open wires
- ❑ Adequate number of circuits and breakers installed
- ❑ Circuits labeled
- ❑ No open spaces in main panel box
- ❑ 20+ amp circuit for kitchen
- ❑ 20+ amp circuit for laundry
- ❑ 30+ amp circuit for heat/AC
- ❑ 30+ amp circuit for hot water (if electric)
- ❑ All receptacles work and are wired correctly (use tester)
- ❑ All switches work
- ❑ All receptacles and switches have covers
- ❑ All overhead lights work
- ❑ All exterior receptacles work and are GFCI protected
- ❑ All appropriate kitchen and bathroom receptacles are GFCI protected
- ❑ All GFCI receptacles are located and marked

Chapter 14

PHASE 6 CONSTRUCTION:
FINAL COMPLETION

At this point, you are now in the homestretch of your house construction. The exterior of the house is finished, but the grounds need final grading, landscaping, and the final driveway. The interior requires some detailed finish work, including final painting, installation of door, closet, and bathroom hardware, final cleaning, and carpeting. These items will put the finishing touches on your house, so attention to detail for each of these areas is a must!

14.1 PAINTING - STAGE 3

Recall that Stage 1 of the paint process was the application of primer and Stage 2 was the application of the first base coat. Now is the time for Stage 3 of painting, which is the application of the last finish coat and completion of all painting. The general rule here is to save this last stage of painting until all the other subcontractors have completed their jobs and won't be around to nick, scrape, or leave marks on any of the walls. If the preparation and work from Stage 1 and

Stage 2 were done correctly, this final coat of paint will be smooth, consistent, and will last many years.

14.2 HARDWARE: DOORS, CLOSETS, AND BATHROOMS

Now that the painting is complete, the door, closet, and bathroom hardware can be installed. This hardware includes all doorknobs, closet rods and shelving, and bathroom towel racks and toilet paper holders. The installation of this hardware is relatively simple for most people and can be performed without the need for a separate subcontractor. But be aware that there are more doorknobs and towel racks than you may have realized, and closet design and hardware installation is not trivial if you want to do it right. Be prepared to spend at least 2 or 3 days of planning and gathering materials, and 2 or 3 or more long days installing this hardware if you have an average sized house. This time, of course, will vary with the size of your home and your level of experience. But in any case, it will probably take you longer than you think to get this job done.

But no matter what your level of experience, it is wise to: 1) plan your closets in detail, 2) know how many and what type of doorknobs you need, 3) know how many and what size of towel racks and bathroom hardware that you need, and 4) have all the hardware on site and ready to go before you start. This will save you a lot of time and hassle by helping to prevent extra trips to the store and getting all this hardware installed efficiently and correctly.

HELPFUL HINT: Use pre-packaged closet kits that fit the size, shape, and needs for each of your closets. These kits are relatively easy to install and are sold at most large home centers. Get the heaviest-duty version available, and try to avoid the cheap, flimsy materials that may not stand up over time.

14.3 FINAL CLEANING

The final cleaning is necessary to bring the interior to a brand new, immaculate condition. This involves removing and scrubbing all dust and debris from floors, windows, window sills, cabinets, shelves, countertops, vents, sinks, toilets, bathtubs, showers, and any other surface or fixture in the house. This is not an easy job, but can be done by you and a few dedicated family members that are armed with the right cleaning supplies and equipment.

There are subcontractors that specialize in cleaning new construction houses, and they have the experience and equipment to do the job quickly, efficiently, and effectively. I hired a specialized company to come in and do the final cleaning for my house, and it was worth every penny. The crew of four had the complete interior of my house spotless in less that 8 hours. This same job would have probably taken me and my family members 2 or 3 days to complete.

14.4 CARPETING

Carpeting can be installed before or after the final cleaning, and is basically a matter of preference. But the bottom line here is to wait as long as possible to install your carpeting to help avoid any marks or stains caused by other subcontractors or the construction process.

There are many grades and styles of carpet, and your flooring subcontractor can explain your many options to you. But be aware that you get what you pay for with carpeting. A cheap carpet may look worn quickly and last only a few years, while a better grade of carpet can withstand more foot traffic and frequent cleanings and still look good after many years.

HELPFUL HINT: Always buy the best padding available for your carpet. Your flooring subcontractor can tell you which is best. This is the cheapest and best way to ensure that you will get the maximum life from your carpeting.

14.5 DRIVEWAY

The completion of the driveway involves covering it with asphalt, concrete, more gravel, or other material that is common in your area. A finished driveway is a welcome relief because it puts an end to the months of dirt and mud that you and your subcontractors had to drive through and walk through for many months.

No matter what type of finished driveway you choose, it is wise to wait until the very end of construction to complete your driveway. This helps to avoid any heavy truck traffic (delivery trucks, concrete trucks, cranes, etc.) that may damage your new and finished driveway.

HELPFUL HINT: A good, compact base layer is absolutely essential for your driveway. Be sure to thoroughly discuss this with your driveway subcontractor.

14.6 LANDSCAPING

Landscaping involves bringing in any needed fill dirt or topsoil, establishing the final grade, filling in any low areas, establishing swales to divert water (if necessary), and planting grass, trees, and shrubs. Although you may choose to do all or part of the landscaping yourself, a landscaping subcontractor is a must if you have large areas that require topsoil and grading, or if you have significant amounts of re-grading that require heavy tractors or equipment to accomplish.

Establishing the final grade is perhaps the most important part of the landscaping process. You must establish a slope away from the foundation at all sides of the house to help divert water away from the foundation. If this is not possible because of higher ground on one or more sides of the house, then you must establish a swale in that area. A swale is a depression in the ground that is between the house and the higher ground that will carry any water away from the foundation. Diverting water away from the foundation around the entire perimeter of your home is critical and must be done.

HELPFUL HINT: Add a few extra inches of topsoil or fill for the slope around the perimeter of your house, immediately next to the foundation. This is because the fill around the foundation will sink a few inches over the next year or two.

HELPFUL HINT: The first line of defense against water intrusion in basements or foundations is not the underground perimeter drain or foundation slope, but a good roof gutter and downspout system. The downspouts must be extended to deposit water at least 8 to 10 feet away from and down slope from the foundation. Underground drain pipes and pop-up type drain outlets in the ground work well for this, and can be easily installed by your landscape contractor at this time. Depositing rainwater well away from the foundation is one of the single most important things you can do to prevent water intrusion!

HELPFUL HINT: Make sure you purchase a type of grass seed that is well known and used in your area. Any local landscaping subcontractor will know what grass types can survive the sun, shade, and drought and soil conditions for your area.

HELPFUL HINT: When planting trees and shrubs, always develop and use a landscaping plan and always consider the full grown sizes of trees and shrubs, and not how they appear at the store or nursery.

14.7 FINAL PUNCH LIST

At this point, construction may appear to be complete, but there may still be many little items and details that need to be performed to finish the job. This list of items is commonly referred to as the final punch list. Depending on your or your many subcontractors' attention to detail, this list can be very long or very short.

These items can include repairing dings in walls, touching up paint, adjusting sticky doors or windows, lining up door latches correctly, installing numbers on the front of the house, installing a mail box, repairing any leaking faucets of fixtures, installing light bulbs, adjusting loose electrical receptacles, getting rid of any extra construction materials, or any other minor item that needs to be adjusted or repaired.

At this point, congratulations! The construction of your house is now complete. But wait, there are still a few things you need to do to complete the home building process. These items are covered in the next section.

14.8 CLOSE OUT FINANCES AND ACCOUNTS

It is now time to close out your accounts and straighten out your finances. This process involves making sure all of your subcontractors have been paid, closing out your accounts with suppliers, gathering the necessary lien waivers from your major subcontractors (refer to Chapter 5), obtaining your occupancy permit, completing your final draw and necessary paperwork for your construction loan, and converting your construction loan into a typical mortgage loan. If this all seems complicated now, do not worry because your lending institution is there and very willing to help you with every step of this final close out process.

Chapter 15

SUMMARY

The information presented in this book has shown you a proven process on how to successfully subcontract and build your own new home. The seemingly complex and complicated process of building your own home has been broken down into small, manageable steps and organized into an easy-to-use procedure that almost anyone can follow and use.

If you feel uncomfortable with any area of the home construction process, then you are encouraged to seek out more information in that particular area. There are many books and web sites available that can easily provide any detailed knowledge or additional information that you may need. But again, as emphasized throughout this book, use your subcontractors as your hired experts to help you and to answer any questions or concerns that you may have about any particular area.

You are encouraged to read through the processes and procedures in this book again, make copies of the schedules and checklists, and use them to help give you the confidence that you need to get started. You can do it! Pay extra attention to your house requirements and the weekly schedule form, as these will be important keys to your success. Best wishes to you!

For additional information and possible updates to this book, please go to:

www.HomeBuildingBook.com

For information on the author's book on becoming a home inspector, please go to:

www.HomeInspectionBook.com